LIFE NATURE LIBRARY

THE
PLANTS

OTHER BOOKS
BY THE EDITORS OF LIFE

LIFE NATURE LIBRARY

THE PLANTS

by Frits W. Went
and The Editors of LIFE

TIME INCORPORATED
NEW YORK

A
STONEHENGE
BOOK

About the Author

Frits W. Went is the son of one botanist and the father of another. His youth was spent in Utrecht, Holland, where his father taught at the University's Botanical Gardens and Institute. In constant contact with botanists and plant research, he decided to take up the science himself. Soon after receiving his doctorate from Utrecht, Dr. Went moved to Indonesia to spend five years at the famous Botanical Gardens at Buitenzorg (Bogor), Java. In 1933 he came to the California Institute of Technology, where he became professor of plant physiology and remained until 1958.

A pioneer in the field of plant hormones, Dr. Went in recent years has turned to the study of environmental influences on plant growth. Over 15 years of work in both areas are summarized in his book *The Experimental Control of Plant Growth*. Dr. Went's interest in plant ecology has its fullest expression in his present position as Director of the Missouri Botanical Garden in St. Louis. Here, in the Climatron—a climate-controlled display greenhouse that he designed— plants from a wide variety of habitats are under investigation.

A member of the National Academy of Sciences and of many other scientific societies, Dr. Went has served as president of both the Botanical Society of America and the American Society of Plant Physiologists and is the author of more than 150 technical papers.

ON THE COVER: Spread out like wind-tossed banners, the red, white and green leaves of a caladium suggest the beauty and diversity of all plants. Caladium, once a jungle-growing rarity, is an ornamental plant in many homes today.

Contents

TIME INC. BOOK DIVISION

Editor: NORMAN P. ROSS

Copy Director: WILLIAM JAY GOLD   *Art Director:* EDWARD A. HAMILTON

Chief of Research: BEATRICE T. DOBIE

EDITORIAL STAFF FOR "THE PLANTS"

Editor, LIFE Nature Library: MAITLAND A. EDEY

Assistant to the Editor: JOHN PURCELL

Copy Editor: PERCY KNAUTH

Designer: PAUL JENSEN

Staff Writers: DALE BROWN, DORIS BRY, MARY LOUISE GROSSMAN, ALFRED LANSING

Chief Researcher: MARTHA TURNER

Researchers: GERALD A. BAIR, ELEANOR FELTSER, LECLAIR G. LAMBERT, PAULA NORWORTH,
CAROL PHILLIPPE, MARJORIE M. PICKENS, SUSAN RAYFIELD, ROXANNA SAYRE,
PAUL W. SCHWARTZ, NANCY SHUKER, IRIS S. UNGER

Picture Researchers: MARGARET K. GOLDSMITH, BARBARA SULLIVAN

Art Associate: ROBERT L. YOUNG

Art Assistants: JAMES D. SMITH, MARK A. BINN, ERIC GLUCKMAN

Copy Staff: MARIAN GORDON GOLDMAN, JOAN CHAMBERS, DOLORES A. LITTLES

Publisher: JEROME S. HARDY

General Manager: JOHN A. WATTERS

LIFE MAGAZINE

Editor	*Managing Editor*	*Publisher*
EDWARD K. THOMPSON	GEORGE P. HUNT	C. D. JACKSON

The text for the chapters of this book was written by Frits W. Went, the picture essays by the editorial staff. The following individuals and departments of Time Inc. were helpful in producing the book: Alfred Eisenstaedt, Eliot Elisofon, Fritz Goro and Dmitri Kessel, LIFE staff photographers; Doris O' Neil, Chief of the LIFE Picture Library; Clara Applegate of the TIME-LIFE News Service; and Content Peckham, Chief of the Time Inc. Bureau of Editorial Reference.

Introduction

ALTHOUGH we accept as axiomatic the fact that plants are green, their green pigment, chlorophyll, is remarkable in the biological world. It makes plants, quite literally, providers of energy to the world's host of living organisms—man and all the other animals, and even nongreen plants. For it is chlorophyll that gives plants the unique ability to utilize the energy of sunlight for the manufacture of food; and this in turn means that fungi and animals can use plant compounds for energy and for their own building materials, either directly or through complex food chains. And to man, of course, plants furnish thousands of other useful products beyond the primary benefits of food.

We know from the fossil record that plants appeared on this earth hundreds of millions of years ago. Although the actual origin of living matter continues to be a controversial question, it is likely that the earliest living "organisms," whose composition is unknown, derived the energy for growth and reproduction by simple chemical means. Presumably they broke down chemical compounds in their watery environment; eventually they utilized the sunlight by means of photoreceptive pigments. However it occurred, from some unknown, primitive green organism the continuous process of evolution has given us all the wonderfully diverse and fascinating world of plants we live in today. They are found almost everywhere, and the adaptations they have made to special environments, as the cactus family has to deserts, are as extraordinary as anything in nature.

As man learns more about plants, how they are constructed, how they function and react to their habitat, he also learns how to modify and even to control their growth and behavior. It is scarcely necessary to point out the importance of this to our well-being. Hybrid corn, antibiotics, herbicides and growth hormones are only some of the developments which have reached far beyond the plant sciences into our public health, our national economy and even our sociology.

Dr. Frits Went, an outstanding botanist with an unusually broad understanding of his subject, has joined with the Editors of LIFE to produce a book which beautifully summarizes and illustrates the basic structure, activities and behavior of plants. This is no superficial work, although author and editors have dropped a hint here and there to indicate how much more there is to the whole story than can be told in a book of this size. I am sure that many readers, once they have been introduced to botany in these pages, will find themselves with an irresistible urge to pursue further many of these fascinating bypaths and ramifications of a science that is basic to our world.

WILLIAM CAMPBELL STEERE
Director, The New York Botanical Garden
Professor of Botany, Columbia University

1

The
Green World

BOTANY, the study of plants, occupies a peculiar position in the history of
human knowledge. For many thousands of years it was the one field of
awareness about which man had anything more than the vaguest of insights. It
is impossible to know today just what our Stone Age ancestors knew about
plants, but from what we can observe of primitive societies that still exist, a
detailed learning of plants and their properties must be extremely ancient.
This is logical. Plants are the basis of the food pyramid for all living things,
even other plants. They have always been enormously important to the welfare
of peoples, not only for food, but also for clothing, weapons, tools, dyes, medicines, shelter and a great many other purposes. Tribesmen living today in the
jungles of the Amazon recognize literally hundreds of plants and know many
properties of each. To them botany, as such, has no name and is probably not
even recognized as a special branch of "knowledge" at all. It is something more
basic, a part of life itself, so fundamental and necessary that to exist without it
would be impossible.

Unfortunately, the more civilized we become the farther away we move from
direct contact with plants, and the less distinct our knowledge of botany grows.

Yet everyone comes unconsciously on an amazing amount of botanical knowledge, and few people will fail to recognize a rose, an apple or an orchid. When Neolithic man, living in the Middle East about 10,000 years ago, discovered certain grasses that could be harvested, and their seeds planted for richer yields the next season, the first great step in a new association of plants and men was taken. Grains were discovered and from them flowed the marvel of agriculture: cultivated crops. From then on, man would increasingly take his living from the controlled production of a few plants, rather than getting a little here and a little there from many varieties that grew wild—and the accumulated knowledge of tens of thousands of years of experience and intimacy with plants in the wild would begin to fade away.

By the beginning of the 18th Century, botany as a science concerned itself primarily with the cataloguing and naming of plants. A textbook written at that time (in Latin, of course) defined it as "that branch of science by which one can in the happiest and quickest way name the largest number of plants." This is hardly a recommendation to prospective students, and indeed, if economics is known as the dismal science, certainly classical botany was deservedly known among students as the next most dismal. I emphasize *classical* botany, because in the last century or so there has been a profound change in our approach to the subject. Today it takes in dozens of other sciences, ranging all the way from biochemistry to geography. It touches human history, sociology and economics in scores of places. It gives us insights into the origins of life and the processes of evolution. It is an intensely interesting subject, but very few people have had a chance to realize that it has so greatly changed. It is no surprise to me, therefore, that when I take a group of beginning botany students into the field for the first time I find them bored, anxious to get the course over with so that they can gain the credits and get on to something more vital, like Anglo-Saxon runes.

My habit on a field trip is to start asking new students the name of every plant we see. Naturally, since they are mostly city-bred, they hardly recognize any of them, become increasingly lackadaisical and soon are reduced to a refrain of sullen "I don't knows." At this point they are in the right frame of mind to be jarred into activity, so I pick up a grass.

"What is this?" I ask.

"We don't know any grasses," someone will say.

"Well, there you are," I reply. "You just told me the name of the family of this plant—the grasses, or Gramineae. I myself know only a few individual species of grass, not many more than you do. But like you, I can tell a corn plant from a bamboo, and rice from wheat. Now if you will only use your eyes and start looking at this grass a little more closely, you will see that it has small but beautiful and delicate flowers. Look still more closely, and you will see the tiny stigmas sticking out of the tops of the blossoms, ready to catch pollen grains borne on the wind so that the plant may be fertilized and capable of reproduction. You may also see the anthers, or pollen sacs, suspended from their threadlike filaments, waving back and forth in the breeze, scattering their pollen to fertilize other plants nearby."

By this time a few students are down on their hands and knees actually looking at the grass and I ask another question: "Why do some plants have big, showy flowers while grasses have such tiny, inconspicuous ones?" This, too, usually draws a blank, so I explain that it has to do with pollination. "All

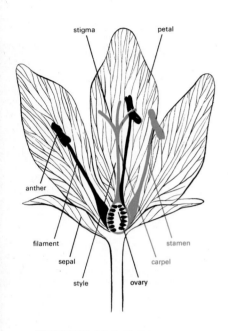

ANATOMY OF A FLOWER

The various parts of a flower are named and located on this cutaway view of an idealized blossom. The two kinds of sexual organs are shown in color. At the center is the female carpel with a seed-containing ovary forming its base and pollen-catching stigmas (three in this example) topping the slender, supporting style. Each of the adjacent male stamens consists of two parts: the supporting filament and the pollen-producing anther. Carpel and stamens are surrounded by the petals, and this whole array, in turn, is embraced by the sepals that once enclosed the entire complex structure in a tiny bud.

flowering plants must be pollinated so that they can produce fertile seeds. Some plants pollinate themselves, some are pollinated by insects or even birds or bats, and some by the wind. If insects are to do the job, the plant must have striking or fragrant blossoms to attract them, but wind does its work anyway, so that wind-pollinated plants do not need to grow large and showy flowers."

The next plant I pick shows no flowers at all. All the interest I was able to stir up about the grass plant seems lost. But after I have explained that a good botanist uses all his senses, not just his eyes, to recognize a plant, a few students will gingerly take hold of the leafy branch, smell it, and in amazement say: "This smells like mint." Upon which I assure them that they have indeed correctly identified the plant; it is a mint or, in Latin, Mentha.

T HE next plant I hold up for examination arouses more interest. By now my students are wondering whether there are any other plant characteristics than those that can be seen or smelled which might give a clue to identity. They sniff, and smell nothing. I ask them to crush the leaves and smell again. The plant still has no peculiar odor. But just as they are about to throw the leaves away, they finally detect a faintly aromatic scent which grows stronger and stronger. Moreover, there is something hauntingly familiar about it, and one or two students at last identify it: the odor is that of bitter almonds and is produced by benzaldehyde, a chemical well known to any laboratory worker. The plant is a wild cherry, and the smell identifies it as a member of the Rosaceae, or rose family.

But why is the benzaldehyde odor not immediately apparent? The answer lies in the plant's chemical make-up. Many members of the rose family contain a substance known as amygdalin, which is one of many so-called glucosides, or sugar containers. Glucosides are complex chemicals in which a sugar is chemically combined with hydrocyanic acid and benzaldehyde or some other chemical. Sugars themselves are nonvolatile, hence they have no odor. Neither does a glucoside if it is left intact, as is the amygdalin in the wild cherry leaf. But if the leaf is crushed by rubbing it firmly back and forth between the fingers, this frees certain enzymes which act as catalysts to split the amygdalin molecules, liberating both the hydrocyanic acid and the benzaldehyde, and there is the typical bitter-almond smell. Thus, in a leaf of this kind, we not only find a means of identifying the plant's family but we get a beginner's lesson in plant chemistry into the bargain.

Other plants can be recognized by tasting. Most members of the mustard family, for example, contain mustard oils and can be identified by the tongue: even as seedlings they have a mustardlike flavor. And the family of umbellifers can be recognized by a rather sharp, aromatic flavor, easily noted in cumin, anise, celery or parsnip. At this point, I explain to my students that few plants are so poisonous that it is dangerous merely to taste them. Certain mushrooms, of course, are poisonous if chewed up and swallowed. But only poison ivy, poison oak and poison sumac are dangerous even to touch—in most persons they will cause a severe skin irritation. Many plants, however, are intensely bitter, so it is advisable first to lick the cut edge carefully before starting to chew, and then spit out rather than swallow the sample.

Thus, at the end of their first practical class in botany, my students learn that they can tell the name of the genus or family of about half the plants they see growing in field or forest simply by using all their senses and by applying information they already possess. This is an important lesson, for it embodies

WHEAT

BREEZE OR BEES

All conifers and many flowering plants are wind-pollinated. Wheat (above) has an inconspicuous flower (detail) from which protrude both the male anthers that loose their pollen on the wind and the feathery female stigmas that await the pollen which will be airborne to them from the neighboring wheat plants. Insect-pollinated plants, such as the tulip (below), often have brightly colored flowers and may secrete nectar. Plants which are fertilized in this efficient way produce lesser quantities of pollen and have simpler female organs than those which are dependent on the vagaries of the wind.

TULIP

the simple principles on which a rough-and-ready classification of plants has long been based: when you come across a plant you do not know, look at it, smell it, crush it, taste it to find what characteristics it has in common with plants you do know.

This kind of classification is still commonplace among country folk. Primitive people in particular, whose living depends on the plants and animals of their native surroundings, obviously *must* be able to tell various plants and trees apart: they must know which ones have edible leaves or fruits, which can be used as rope, which contain arrow or fish poison and which can be used as medicine. From these everyday uses come the descriptive names that express the properties of many plants, like wormwood or catnip or bloodroot.

I T was this sort of outdoor recognition, practiced by those who collected medicinal herbs in the woods, that formed the basis of botany in most of the world until the 16th Century. At about that time the traditional methods began to be altered so that botany could be taught to medical students in universities and, moreover, could be taught out of books. Taste and smell and feel gradually gave way to properties that could be more easily described in words or pictures, such as leaf shape, color or flower characteristics. Finally the famous Swedish botanist, Carl von Linné, known to the world by his Latin name Linnaeus, hit upon a simple and very useful method of plant identification. The number of stamens in a flower, he pointed out, is always the same in the same kind of plant—any flower in the amaryllis family, for instance, always has six stamens, members of the morning-glory family always have four, the flowers of the iris family have three.

Linnaeus' classification system was most effective, but he himself realized that it was not a "natural" system. The trouble was that plants having the same number of stamens are not necessarily the most closely related—or vice versa. For instance, the mint, with its strong odor, opposite leaves, square stem, two-lipped flower and four stamens, is obviously closely related to the sages, which share exactly these same characteristics—except that the sages have only two stamens. A more natural, and hence more accurate, system would be one that classifies plants by their ancestry and evolutionary development. This is the now generally accepted system that has gradually been evolved by botanical taxonomists, one that reflects the ways in which the more complicated plants seem to have developed from the more primitive ones that first flourished on earth hundreds of millions of years ago.

The simplest oxygen-producing plants—which presumably resemble the first ones that developed on the earth—are known generally as algae. There are several kinds of algae, the most primitive being the blue-green algae, tiny organisms that grow for the most part in fresh water and cause the characteristic dark green scum on ponds that have been polluted or overfertilized with manure. Blue-green algae are sometimes single-celled but more often come in clusters, threads or chains. However, they never form more complex organizations, nor can they reproduce sexually. Their cells are less than 1/2,500 of an inch long and can be seen with the naked eye only when present in enormous numbers.

Slightly more complex and much more numerous, the green algae are found in fresh or salt water, floating or attached to whatever may be there, or sometimes swimming by beating whiplike flagellae. They too cause so-called seasonal "blooms" on the surfaces of bodies of water.

Why are not all lakes, or for that matter all the seas and oceans, filled with

A SACRED LILY

The first paintings of plants may have been inspired by man's interest in their value as medicines or by his impulse to give plants some religious significance. These Madonna lilies form a part of a Cretan mural painted about 1550 B.C. At that time the lily was regarded as a symbol of fruitfulness. It was also the sacred emblem of the goddess who protected hunters, fishermen and sailors.

these green algae? The reason is that algae need nutrients, just as corn and cotton do, in order to grow and multiply. Only where large amounts of phosphates and nitrates wash into the water from the adjacent land will algae develop in large masses. Thus while they may grow in the ocean waters close to shore, they cannot live farther out at sea because there are hardly any nutrients there for them to absorb, which explains why the open ocean is not green.

In the course of evolution, in which larger and more complicated organisms began to develop from simpler ones, multicellular algae gradually appeared. Their several cells were either loosely associated—as in *Volvox*, which consists of small colonies of green flagellated cells found in pools of fresh water—or they hung together in long, hairlike threads, as in *Spirogyra*, a common alga of ponds and streams. In time, more complex types of green algae evolved—for example, *Ulva*, known as sea lettuce, and *Chara*, a member of the stonewort family. All of these, because of their color, are placed in the class of green algae.

Another group is of a generally brown color, hence its members are named the brown algae. The giant kelps, the largest sea algae in existence, belong to this group. They are found along the coasts of the colder parts of the oceans, attached to stones or rocks; in offshore beds they form great stems, up to 300 feet long or more in some species. Short-stemmed brown algae are also found in tidal pools. A fourth group is red in color and consequently called the red algae. They also occur along seashores, often intermixed with brown algae, but never reaching the enormous size of the kelps. Finally, there are the euglenoids, found in stagnant pools; diatoms and dinoflagellates, which make up most of the plankton in the ocean; and the golden algae, which form fresh-water plankton.

A LOGICAL question presents itself here: Why, if they are so ancient and so primitive, and if other plants have evolved from them, do the algae themselves still exist? The answer is that the algae are at the same time extremely well adapted to their environment. Other plants may have exploited other environments in endless ways, but that does not mean that the same old efficient *unchanged* algae could not go on as they always had, so long as they had water, dissolved chemicals and sunlight. For the algae all share with the majority of other plants a common characteristic: they contain a green pigment known as chlorophyll, the vital agent that absorbs the sun's light energy and can change it into the chemical energy that plants need for growth.

Plants that feed themselves from sunlight are among the autotrophic, or self-feeding, plants. Obviously, they can grow only where there is enough light, and without exception they have chlorophyll, even if all of them do not show it in the familiar green plant color. Many of the different-colored algae, for instance, have chlorophyll that is masked with brown or red pigments; but if the cells containing these pigments die, the masking color will often wash away with time, revealing the green chlorophyll.

With the exception of some bacteria, plants that do not contain chlorophyll cannot produce their own food. Like animals, they must get their energy ultimately from green plants. Such plants do not need to live in the light; they may grow in the soil or in other dark places. They belong to two groups: the bacteria, microscopic in size, nonsexual in reproduction and as simple in form as the simplest algae; and the far larger and far more complicated fungi.

Fungi are still low on the scale of plant evolution; they have developed to a certain extent parallel with the algae, but differ from them in not having chlorophyll. A fungus consists basically of a quantity of hairlike threads, such as the

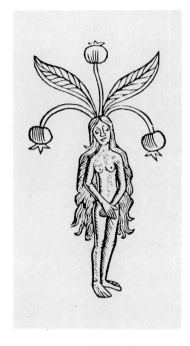

THE MAGIC MANDRAKE

Oldest of "magical" plants, the mandrake was revered as far back as Genesis for its alleged aphrodisiac powers, and its use as a drug persists even today. In Greece, Circe stirred mandrake into her potion for turning men into swine. Because its forked roots resemble legs, the mandrake was often depicted in medieval Europe as a tiny human figure, as in this 1498 French drawing of a "female" root.

fuzzy "mold" sometimes found on a piece of stale bread. Sometimes these threads, or hyphae, join together to form a large organized structure—for example, a mushroom. But the mushroom or toadstool that one sees poking its head up from the forest floor is only the visible spore-producing part of the fungus. The mushroom forms when the fungus is ready to reproduce itself, but its continuing and more fundamental part is the unseen web of hyphae hidden in the soil. These minute threads can grow through the smallest holes, which makes it possible for fungi to penetrate plant and animal bodies wherever the body surface is injured. Once inside, the threads range far and wide, infecting bodies and taking nourishment from the individual cells of their host. Hundreds of plant diseases, among them smut, rust, wilt and late blight, are the result of fungi operating in this way, as well as dozens of diseases in animals and man.

Not all fungi, however, are harmful. Together with bacteria, they decompose plant litter on the forest floor, freeing vital carbon dioxide and other carbon components from the skeletons of leaves and the dead wood of branches and tree trunks, and leaving rich humus behind. The special fungi known as yeasts carry out all sorts of useful chemical reactions, such as the formation of alcohol from sugars, while other fungi produce such important antibiotics as penicillin and aureomycin, as well as less glamorous but hardly less vital products like vitamins and citric acid.

THE lichens are another remarkable group of primitive plants, tougher than any others. Some of them form colorful crusts on the surface of rocks, others cover the bark of trees. High on mountains or far north in the Arctic, where other plants can scarcely grow because of the extreme cold, lichens are the main forms of plant life; indeed, in the Antarctic they are the predominant plants found. But when a thin slice cut from a lichen is examined under the microscope, it is found to consist of not one but two separate plants: an alga (either a blue-green or a green) and a fungus, whose threadlike hyphae are woven together into a tough skin surrounding the algae. The algae, with their chlorophyll, provide energy from sunlight for the partnership, and the fungi provide mineral food and proper shelter. This is a case of true symbiosis, where two completely different organisms live together, mutually aiding each other and producing new and strange forms beyond the capacity of either alga or fungus by itself.

Although the relatively simple organisms described so far are all plants, and although they populate the oceans and much of the earth's surface, as yet there has been no mention made of the organisms that most of us usually think of as plants. What about them? What about the trees, shrubs and herbs, the colorful flowers and green leaves that carpet the land? Where do they fit into the picture; when and how did they begin to evolve?

Land plants developed considerably later in time than algae, of which the earliest traces appear in deposits about two billion years old. The first suspected remains of land plants in fossil form are about 420 million years old, and 390 million years ago there was a well-developed vegetation along lake shores and other moist areas. These early land species go by the name of vascular plants because of the internal plumbing systems that they had. They reproduced by means of microscopic spores formed in little sacs on their stems or leaves. For many millions of years, such spore plants—psilophytes, ferns, horsetails and club mosses—populated the land areas of the earth. Eventually, tree-sized ferns and giant club mosses were developed, and it was dense forests of these that later

THE FIRST SEED PACKET

Earlier in its life, the pine cone shown above pointed skyward, presenting the egg cells on each of the many scales in its spiral structure to fertilization by wind-borne pollen. Once fertilized, each egg cell grows into a seed, a miniature pine in embryo. Later, as the cone ripens, it turns downward, its scales loosen and the seeds fall to the ground, ready to germinate and grow. This means of reproduction, far more efficient than the broadcast release of spores, first evolved some 300 million years ago. The conifers have been highly successful ever since, but further seed-making advances evolved (opposite).

formed many of our coal deposits. In those days the vegetation was unrelieved by colorful flowers and must have looked a monotonous even green.

During this period, several important innovations appeared, notably a more efficient method of plant reproduction. Spores are comparatively inefficient—out of millions only a few manage to fall on a spot that has the right combination of light and moisture for them to germinate and form sex cells which, after combining, will give rise to a new fern or club moss. By contrast, a seed, which contains a good supply of food and an already partially developed young plant or embryo, all stored together inside a protective casing, has a much better chance to develop into a new plant. Consequently, it is hardly surprising to find some of the ferns and club mosses beginning to develop seeds in the course of evolution. In retrospect, it is easy to see that the seed was one of the great "inventions" of plant evolution, and although many of the early seed bearers are long since extinct, we can still make out a good deal of their history in the record left to us in fossils.

THE earliest seed plants that have survived to the present day are conifers, the members of the pine and spruce family. They are so well adapted to life on earth that in the 300 million years of their existence, there has been relatively little evolutionary change in them. They are among the most successful plants in the world. Pine, spruce and fir populate about a third of all existing forest areas. Where the living is difficult for other plants—in the Arctic, up in the mountains and on the borders of deserts—conifers are usually the last outpost trees. Among the living higher plants, the one with the oldest fossil record, the maidenhair tree, or *Ginkgo*, is related to the conifers.

The adaptation that makes the conifer such a successful plant is its cone. A pine cone is essentially nothing more than a number of specialized spore-bearing "leaves," or scales, concentrated into a tight bunch. On each of these scales one or two large macrospores are formed. After fertilization, this macrospore will give rise to a seed. The structure of the cone, with its hard scales fitting closely together in a spiral pattern, protects the macrospores inside until the cone is ripe. Then the tips of the scales separate. At this time the seeds can actually be shaken out of an open, ripe pine cone, provided birds or squirrels have not already eaten them.

The female cones producing seeds are distinctly larger than other "male" cones on the tree, which produce the sperm cells, or pollen. For fertilization to take place a grain of pollen must come in contact with a female egg cell produced in the macrospore. The only way this can be done among conifers is by the wind. Therefore billions upon billions of pollen grains must be produced to ensure that just a few of them will reach the right spot. If an automobile is parked in a pine forest when the pollen is ripe, it will be dusted with a golden carpet of uncountable numbers of pollen grains that have not found their destination. It is this same enormous excess that at flowering time covers entire lakes with a thin yellow film of pollen.

Some 150 million years after conifers appeared on the face of the earth, the first flowering plants developed. Like the conifers, they were seed bearers, but of a different kind. The big change came when insect pollination entered the picture, and plants began to develop a dazzling variety of flowers to attract them. But despite differences in appearance, a primitive flowering plant such as a magnolia, when compared with a pine tree, still shows a surprising similarity in its mode of reproduction. The one important difference is that the magnolia has

A CRUCIAL ADVANCE

The common magnolia (above) has gone far beyond the pine cone (opposite) in efficiency, just as the pine had advanced beyond the spore-bearing plants. Its egg- and pollen-producing parts grow side by side on the blossom's central spiral. Fertilization is accomplished by pollen-carrying insects, rather than by the wind, and the magnolia's maturing seeds remain hidden within a fleshy ovary until ripe. One of the first plants to evolve these advanced structures, the magnolia is an early member of the enormous company of advanced, flowering plants that dominate the world's present-day flora.

no separate male and female cones—instead, both sexes are present and fulfill their functions in a single flower.

There is a logical reason for this, as there is for most things in nature. As long as the wind does the work of cross-pollination, or fertilization, male and female cones do not have to grow close together. But if insects are to carry the pollen about, proximity of male and female organs makes sense. And if they are in the *same* flower, a single visit from an insect will probably serve the dual purpose of depositing pollen that it is already carrying, and also picking up a fresh supply to carry on to the next flower.

Since an insect moving methodically from flower to flower is infinitely more efficient than the wind in transmitting pollen, it is logical that flowering plants should show a tendency to reduce the amount of pollen formed, especially through reduction in the number of the pollen-bearing stamens. At the same time, as fertilization becomes more efficient, the number of female ovules, or seed bodies, is similarly reduced by a decrease in the number of carpels, or seed leaves. Curiously enough, the flower's petals and sepals (as the bottom or outer petals are called) also have a tendency to decrease in number in the course of evolution from primitive to higher plants.

As a matter of classification, the differences between the more primitive coniferous plants and the more highly evolved flowering ones lie in the way the seeds are placed. In the pine cone the seeds lie exposed, or naked, on the tightly stacked scales, which has led to the term gymnospermae, or naked seed plants. In the magnolia, the carpels close over the seeds, producing a fruit, and hence the magnolia is known as one of the angiospermae, or enclosed-seed plants.

In their efforts to make further distinctions among the 250,000 flowering plants, botanists have seized on a seemingly insignificant character: the number of seedling leaves. Thus we distinguish between dicots, with two such cotyledons, and monocots, which have only one, the latter having evolved later than the dicots. These are paralleled by a number of very obvious differences among mature plants. The majority of monocot leaves, for example, are grasslike, with parallel veins, whereas dicots have mostly broad leaves with herringbone or finger-like veins. Still other differences are found in the flowers, the monocots having their petals and other flower parts mostly in threes, and the dicots mostly in fours or fives.

FURTHER distinctions bring us to the grouping of flowering plants into families: at least 300 different ones are recognized. Their individual species are so numerous that they have never yet been listed in any one book, or even in one series of books. Such a listing would have to describe about a quarter million known plants; to compile it, all the taxonomic botanists in the world would have to work together for years and years, and the finished product would have perhaps half a million pages, enough to cover a whole wall in a library. This seems to bring us a long way from the simple botany walk with which this chapter began —but actually we have learned, as we browsed through these various groups of plants from the algae past the pines to flowering plants, the fundamentals of how they are all arranged in their multifarious kingdom. However, as we saw at the start of this chapter, the ability merely to identify plants is no longer the sole aim of modern botany. It is our purpose in the chapters that follow to look at the plant kingdom in a different way—what plants are made of, how they live and work, and what factors govern their growth, abundance and choice of location throughout the world.

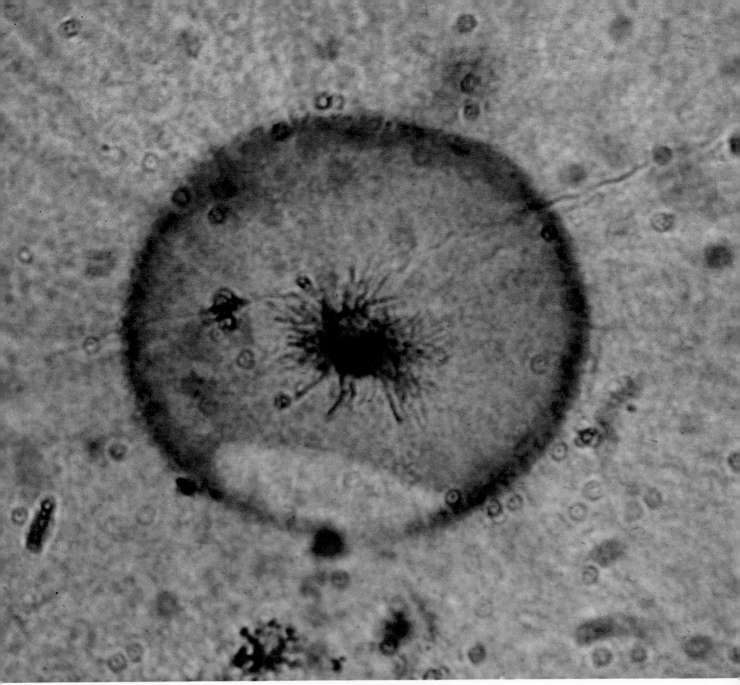

EVIDENCE OF THE EARLIEST KNOWN LIFE ON EARTH, THESE FOSSILIZED BLUE-GREEN ALGAE FROM CANADA MAY BE TWO BILLION YEARS OLD

Conquerors from the Sea

Born of the sea, plants became great conquerors on the land—individually the most widespread and numerous of all living things, filling niches from the deserts to the poles. Yet millions of years elapsed before they evolved even the simplest stalks, leaves and roots. Even today, among the approximately 375,000 living species, there are many still so primitive they hardly seem like plants at all.

17

Tracing Evolution

The seven key steps in the evolution of plants are shown on this chart. The line of progression, running from the bottom left to the top, spans some two billion years. Except for the "Uralgae," the first algae, of which little is known, a representative fossil species or a theoretical reconstruction of one indicates each step. The groups to which these fossil plants belonged are identified; the lines that run from them show how they branched out successfully, giving rise to the living plants arrayed and classified at right. The lines are in two colors to distinguish the thallophytes (blue), with relatively simple plant bodies, from the more structurally complex embryophytes (tan), which include most of the familiar land plants.

Because of gaps in the fossil record, no one is able to say with certainty how the seven groups are related to each other. But paleobotanists assume that as a group branched out it produced at least one offshoot with enough genetic plasticity to make the next great advance. While a new group was forming, the old group continued to evolve, gradually losing its potential for major evolutionary change as its various members became increasingly specialized.

FILICOPHYTA
Devonian—390 million
FIRST TRUE LEAVE

PSILOPHYTA
Silurian—420 million years
FIRST TRUE STEMS

CHLOROPHYTA
Cambrian   600 million years
FIRST ORGANIZED CHLOROPLASTS

"URALGAE"
Pre-Cambrian—about 2 billion years
FIRST OXYGEN-PRODUCING PLANTS

ARCHAIC BACTERIA
Pre-Cambrian—more than 2 billion years
FIRST ORGANIZED LIVING THINGS

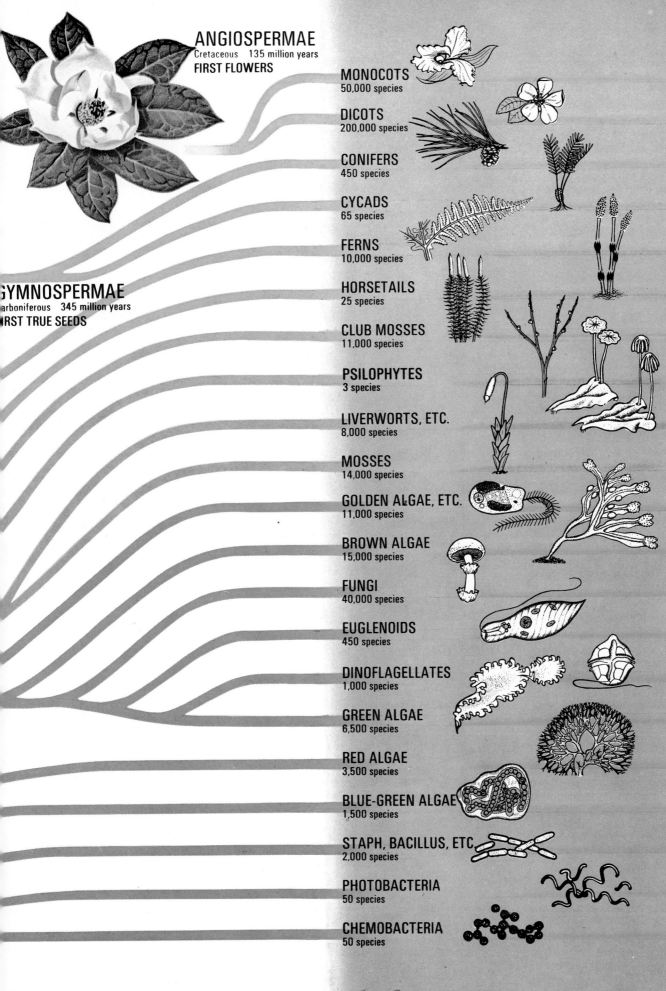

ANGIOSPERMAE
Cretaceous   135 million years
FIRST FLOWERS

MONOCOTS
50,000 species

DICOTS
200,000 species

CONIFERS
450 species

CYCADS
65 species

FERNS
10,000 species

HORSETAILS
25 species

CLUB MOSSES
11,000 species

PSILOPHYTES
3 species

LIVERWORTS, ETC.
8,000 species

MOSSES
14,000 species

GOLDEN ALGAE, ETC.
11,000 species

BROWN ALGAE
15,000 species

FUNGI
40,000 species

EUGLENOIDS
450 species

DINOFLAGELLATES
1,000 species

GREEN ALGAE
6,500 species

RED ALGAE
3,500 species

BLUE-GREEN ALGAE
1,500 species

STAPH, BACILLUS, ETC.
2,000 species

PHOTOBACTERIA
50 species

CHEMOBACTERIA
50 species

GYMNOSPERMAE
arboniferous   345 million years
IRST TRUE SEEDS

Matt Greene

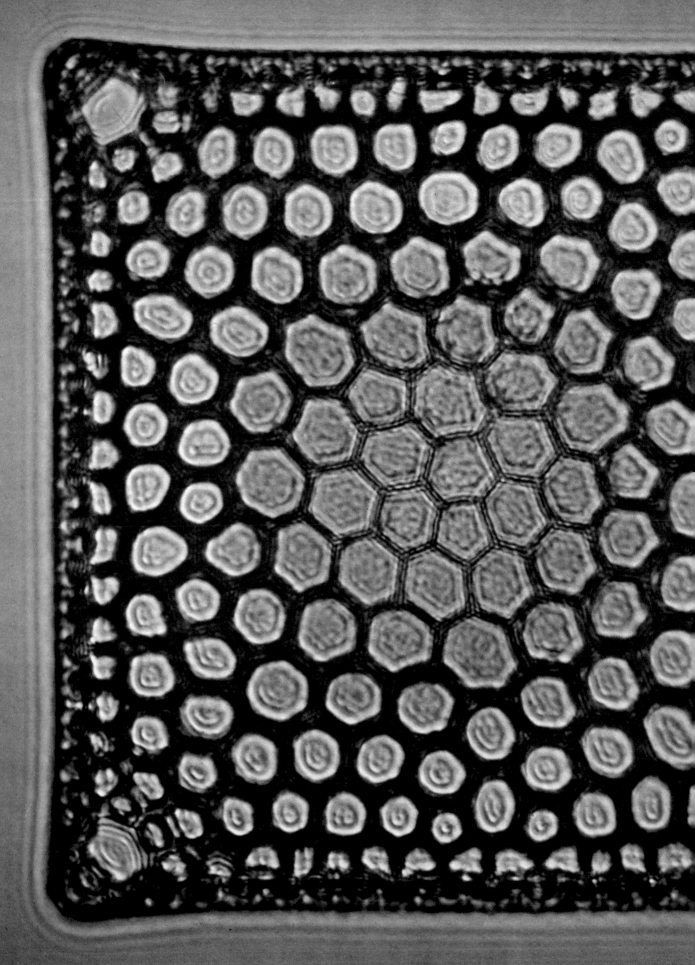

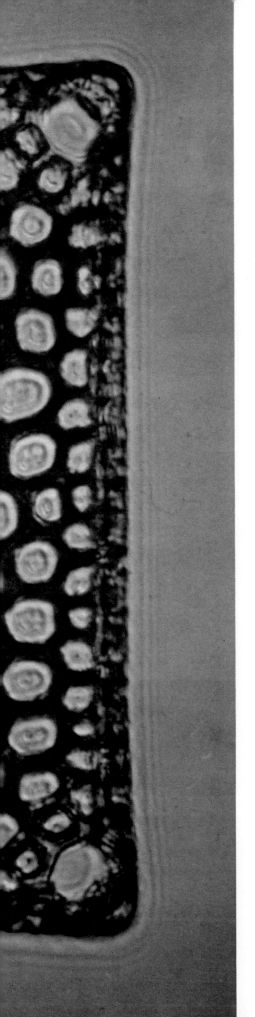

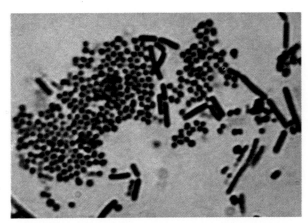

LONG BACILLI AND ROUND COCCI ARE THE COMMONEST BACTERIA

The Tiniest Plants

Smallest and most primitive of the plants, algae and bacteria are found almost everywhere. Algae live not only in fresh and salt water, in colonies and alone, but in the soil, in hot springs, on other plants, on animals and on snow.

Even more ubiquitous than the algae are the bacteria, some of which live right inside us, feeding on living or dead cells, on what we eat and on each other. Bacteria are so small that more than a thousand of the largest species would have to be laid end to end to stretch an inch. There may be 50 million in a drop of liquid and up to 100 million in a pinch of earth.

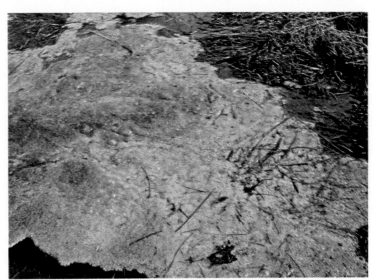

GREEN ALGAE float in a bubbly mass on the surface of shallow water. Already equipped with chlorophyll, algae helped to prepare the primeval world for higher life by manufacturing vital oxygen from water and light.

GEOMETRIC DIATOM, a microscopic alga, has a silica-coated wall comprised of two overlapping halves, like a box with a lid. Normally golden-brown, it has rainbow hues in this photograph because of the refraction of light.

The Scavenging Fungi

Like most bacteria, the fungi have no chlorophyll. They feed on dead or decaying matter or other organisms. They include not only the familiar mushrooms, toadstools and puffballs, but also the slime molds and other similar forms, as well as parasites like smuts, blights and mildews. The slime molds are the most puzzling group, so much so that taxonomists have long disagreed whether to classify them as plants or animals. They seem to have qualities of both. They are made up of streaming masses of protoplasm with many nuclei but no cell walls. And as they fan out, they engulf their food by slowly flowing over it.

ORANGE LICHENS, part fungus, part alga, live on bare rocks in the Arctic.

MOLDS, generally parasites, include *Penicillium*, the source of penicillin.

CUP FUNGI are among the many that convert forest litter into a rich humus.

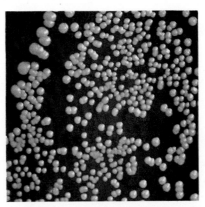

YEASTS, microscopic one-celled plants, are cultured by man for many uses.

LUMINESCENT TOADSTOOLS look normal by day *(top above)*, but glow mysteriously in the dark *(bottom)*, with colors ranging from yellow-orange to blue-green. Many are found on rotting logs in tropical Asian forests, particularly after rain.

SLIME MOLD, animal-like during growth, becomes plantlike in its reproductive phase, when it puts up spore cases. This species, *Stemonitis fusca*, has stalked cases 3/5 of an inch tall, but others may be stemless or grouped together in buttons.

YOUNG HORSETAILS, pointing like minarets from the forest floor, show many features of their earliest forebears. The leaves, dark whorls around joints on the ridged, hollow stems, are only rudimentary, and the branches are mere green spikes. By the Devonian, 390 million years ago, horsetails were widespread; some eventually grew 30 and 40 feet tall.

THE WHISK FERN, *Psilotum nudum*, even today has neither true leaves nor true roots. It closely resembles plants that lived 420 million years ago.

LIVERWORTS, able to differentiate into male and female plants, cluster in damp places. This male *Marchantia* produces sperm in the disks, and rain spreads it to the female plants.

Plants out of the Past

Little changed over millions of years, the rootless, seedless plants shown on these pages offer fascinating clues to the structure and nature of ancient and extinct forms. The leafless whisk fern (*above*) is a direct descendant of some of the first plants to develop woody supporting tissue and an internal plumbing system. The liverwort (*top right*), whose ancestors lived at the same time as those of the whisk fern, failed to evolve such tissue, and as a result never grows more than an inch or two tall. The horsetails (*opposite*) derive some of their rigidity from silica deposited on the cell walls—which led early Americans, who used them as pot scourers, to call them "scouring rushes."

What all these plants have in common is their habit of reproducing by alternate sexless and sexual generations. The whisk fern, for example, releases spores from bulbous cases on its leafless branches. These grow into tiny plants which live underground and are covered with male and female sex organs. In the damp earth, the sperm must swim over to the eggs. After fertilization takes place, a shoot develops and another spore-producing plant emerges.

SMALL CLUB MOSSES like this one retain an early stage of leaf development. Among ancient plants, such tiny leaves improved photosynthesis, heretofore carried on in the stems.

25

FERNS RANGE IN SIZE FROM ONE-QUARTER-INCH WATER PLANTS TO GIANTS LIKE THE TAHITIAN SPECIMEN ABOVE, WHICH GROWS UP TO 60 FEET TAL

The First Leaf Bearers

From their distant past, ferns still keep a leafless, sexual generation that is dependent on water for reproduction. The ferns most familiar to us are actually the sexless generation, the advanced structure which has true leaves and roots. In this they differ markedly from the lower plants. Their fronds take a variety of shapes and sizes, and their spores often appear on the undersides of the fronds. Most fern stems grow laterally underground, though some, as in the giant tree fern above, may protrude as trunks.

26

POLLEN-SPREADING CONIFERS, LIKE THESE SPRUCES AND FIRS, HAVE SUCCESSFULLY SURVIVED IN COOLER, DRIER AND HIGHER REGIONS OF THE EARTH

The First Seed Bearers

As the earliest surviving seed bearers, the still flourishing conifers attest to a revolution in the plant kingdom that allowed vegetation to spread beyond the limited breeding ground of damp earth. For in conifers the male cells are formed in pollen, which can be blown to the female cells by the wind. After fertilization takes place, the seeds are nourished in the female cones until ripe. And since they carry with them their own supply of food, seeds have considerably more chance of surviving than spores do.

27

CROWDING A MEADOW, BLACK-EYED SUSANS THRUST UP FLOWERS TO ATTRACT POLLINATING INSECTS. LIKE MANY OTHER NONWOODY PERENNIAL

The Flowering Plants

More than half of all living plants are classified as flowering plants, or angiosperms—plants with enclosed seeds. These are not only the highest forms of plant life but the most diversified and widespread.

PLANTS OF TEMPERATE REGIONS, THEY CAN SURVIVE WINTER BY DYING DOWN TO THEIR ROOTS IN FALL AND SPROUTING NEW SHOOTS IN SPRING

The angiosperms have been enormously successful for a number of reasons, and the most important of these is the flower, a unique angiosperm structure. The flower is far more efficient reproductively than the separate male and female cones of the conifers. Usually containing both pollen and ovules, it may be pollinated by either the wind, as in the conifers, or by the insects it attracts, or even by itself.

29

Evolving toward Simplicity

The angiosperms, or flowering plants, are divided into two broad groups—the dicots, or dicotyledons, and the monocots, or monocotyledons. Their names underscore their most basic differences: the dicot seed has two or more cotyledons, or seedling leaves, for food storage or for photosynthesis; the monocot contains only one. The paintings at the right show a halved castor bean seed—a dicot—and a monocot corn kernel, with their cotyledons at an early stage of germination. Of the two groups,

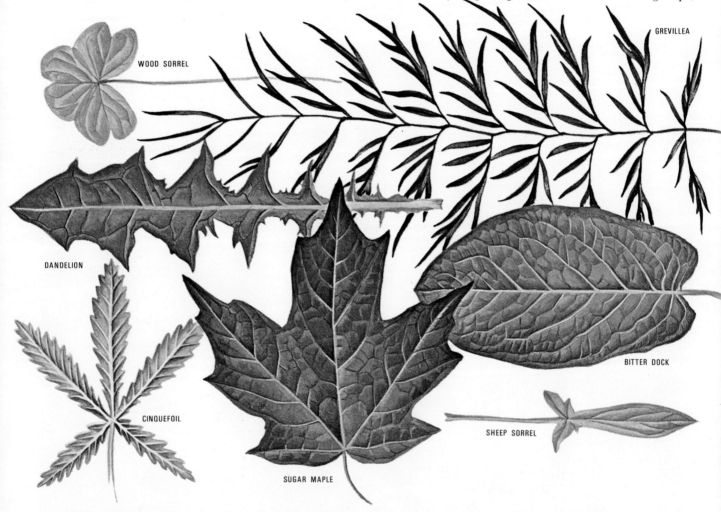

DICOT LEAVES MAY BE ALL IN ONE PIECE LIKE THE BITTER DOCK, COMPOUND LIKE CINQUEFOIL OR DOUBLY COMPOUND AS IN GREVILLEA

BASIC DIFFERENCES of dicots and monocots show up not only in the leaves and seeds, but in the stems, roots and flowers. The typical dicot stem has a center core, the pith, where food is some-times stored, a woody portion which contains the plant's plumbing system, the cortex and the bark. The monocot stem is much simpler, often soft, with vascular bundles scat-

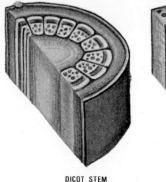

DICOT STEM   MONOCOT STEM

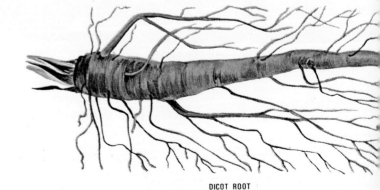

DICOT ROOT

the dicots are the larger by far, with about 200,000 species, including most of the flowering trees and shrubs. The monocots, with about 50,000 species, are the more advanced group, revealing the evolutionary tendency in flowering plants toward a simpler structure with fewer flower parts. The monocots include such diverse families as the lilies, palms, grasses and orchids. The paintings below and on the next two pages by Anne Ophelia Todd Dowden point up differences between the two groups.

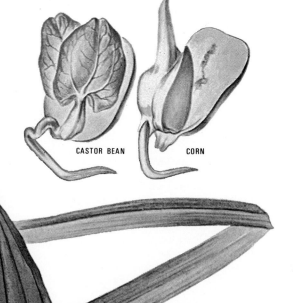

CASTOR BEAN   CORN

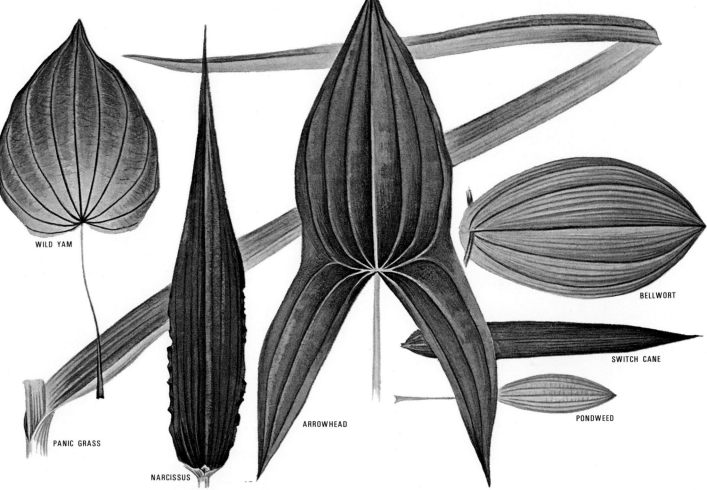

WILD YAM

PANIC GRASS

NARCISSUS

ARROWHEAD

BELLWORT

SWITCH CANE

PONDWEED

PARALLEL-VEINED MONOCOT LEAVES TEND TO BE IN ONE PIECE, LESS VARIED IN SHAPE THAN THOSE OF DICOTS AND LESS INTRICATELY EDGED

tered at random. Dicot roots are generally woody, but monocot roots, attached to nonwoody stems, may be extremely fibrous. Some monocots produce underground structures for reproduction and food storage, such as bulbs and rhizomes. Dicot flowers usually bear sepals and petals in groups of fours and fives, monocot flowers in threes or multiples thereof.

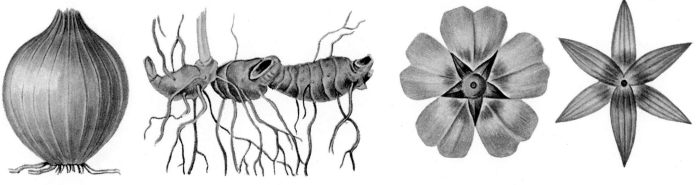

MONOCOT BULB   MONOCOT RHIZOME   DICOT FLOWER   MONOCOT FLOWER

SEDUM

DOGWOOD

BLACK-EYED SUSAN

DICOT SPECIALIZATIONS

Flowers generally simplify as they advance on the evolutionary scale. The sedum *(left, above)* has many parts, the dogwood next to it far fewer. The black-eyed Susan, one of the most advanced, unites many flowers in one blossom *(right)*. Its outer yellow ray of sterile flowers attracts insects, and the inner circle, made up of hundreds of fertile ones, ensures efficient pollination.

COLUMBINE

TOOTHWORT

RED MAPLE

VIOLET

CARDINAL FLOWER

DICOT FLOWERS range from the primitive and multipartite, like the columbine and red maple above, to the simplified, like the cardinal flower, in which the petals as well as the stamens are partially joined.

BUTTERCUP

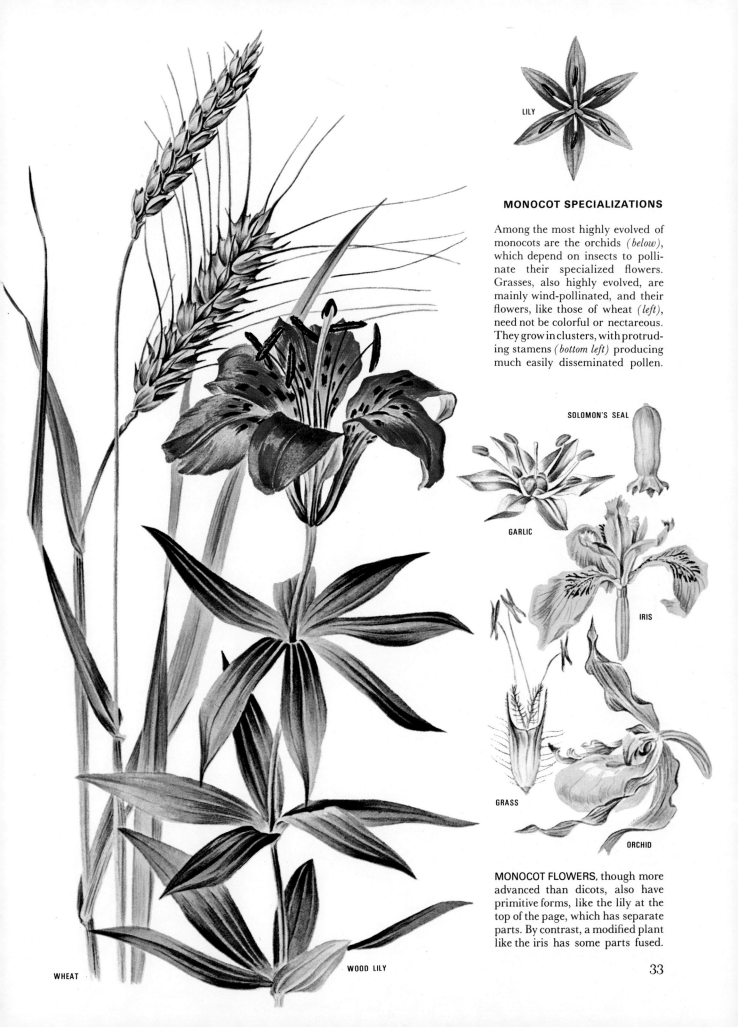

LILY

MONOCOT SPECIALIZATIONS

Among the most highly evolved of monocots are the orchids *(below)*, which depend on insects to pollinate their specialized flowers. Grasses, also highly evolved, are mainly wind-pollinated, and their flowers, like those of wheat *(left)*, need not be colorful or nectareous. They grow in clusters, with protruding stamens *(bottom left)* producing much easily disseminated pollen.

SOLOMON'S SEAL

GARLIC

IRIS

GRASS

ORCHID

MONOCOT FLOWERS, though more advanced than dicots, also have primitive forms, like the lily at the top of the page, which has separate parts. By contrast, a modified plant like the iris has some parts fused.

WHEAT

WOOD LILY

33

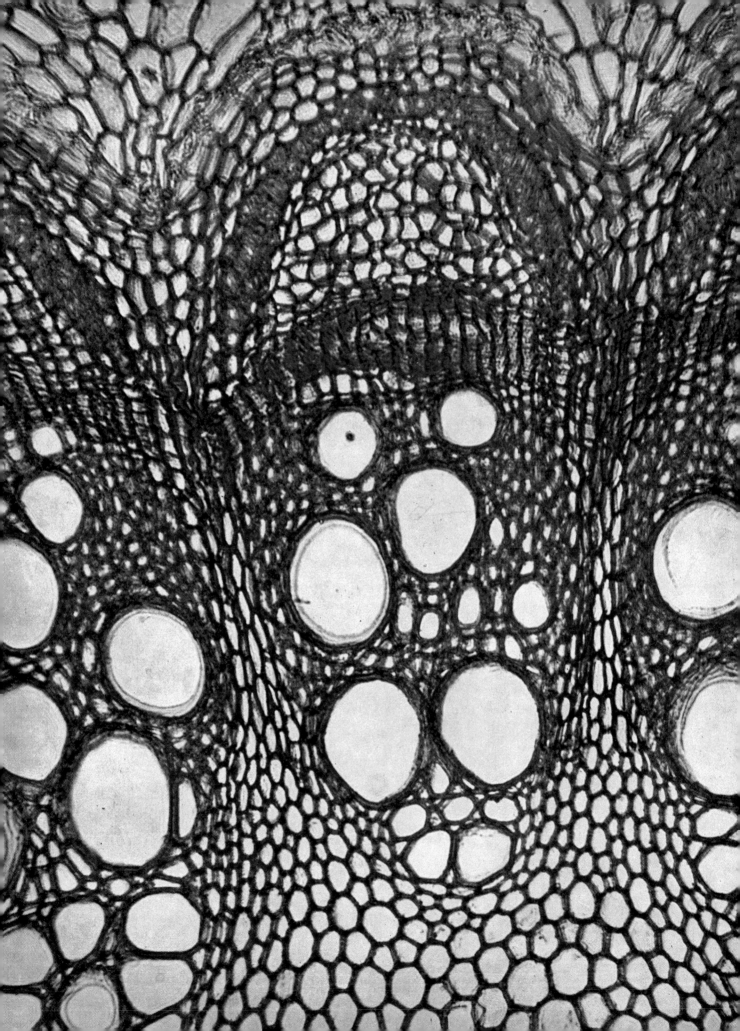

2

The Subworld of the Cell

Before the 17th Century, man knew nothing whatsoever about the fine structure of things. He lived, so to speak, on the surface of the physical world, and even philosophers hardly ventured into the realm where their eyes could penetrate no further. Then, in the years after 1600, the compound microscope and the fine art of lens grinding opened up an entirely new world, the world of microscopic dimensions. It was as revealing as the discovery of the Americas or of electronics or of atomic power. The early microscopists were looked upon with the same awe that we nowadays accord to nuclear physicists and rocketeers. Kings and princes made pilgrimages to Delft in Holland to be shown the wonders of the microworld by Leeuwenhoek, the 17th Century cloth merchant who was the first to discover bacteria, to see blood flow through capillary vessels and to observe living sperm cells.

One of the first discoveries of the early microscopists was that the substance of a plant is not homogeneous. A look at a thin slice of a plant stem or of cork under the microscope revealed that it consisted of a large number of bubbles, or cells, as they were originally called by the Englishman Robert Hooke, their discoverer. Almost 200 years later, in 1839, these general observations were con-

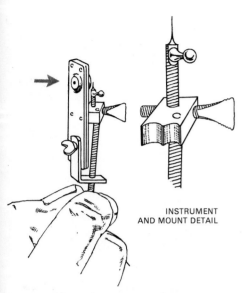

INSTRUMENT
AND MOUNT DETAIL

A HIDDEN WORLD EXPOSED

This single-lens microscope is one of the many instruments made by Anton van Leeuwenhoek, a Dutch merchant and amateur scientist, during the late 1600s. The tiny lens was set between two metal plates (arrow), dry specimens were glued to the pinpoint (detail, right), while wet ones required special mounts. Turns of the horizontal thumb screw and fine adjustments with the knob on the upper screw brought the specimens into focus. For his light, Leeuwenhoek used the sun.

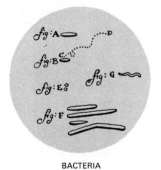

BACTERIA

Five varieties of simple plant life— mouth bacteria—are reproduced here from a sketch by Leeuwenhoek. He found them in matter he scraped from his teeth.

solidated by the German biologists Schleiden and Schwann in the cell theory, which says that every part of a plant or animal consists of cells or of cell products. The cell, therefore, is the basic unit of every plant or animal, and the cell theory is as basic to biology as the molecular and atomic theories are to chemistry and physics. Just as the molecule is the smallest particle which still has the properties of a chemical substance, the cell is the smallest unit which is endowed with life and all the potentialities of the entire organism.

As the power of the microscope grew, scientists were able to penetrate ever deeper into the cell structure, and it became clear that there was far more to the cell than the cell wall, which stands out most clearly under the microscope. Obviously, it was the contents of the cell which bore life. There were many different ways in which this could be demonstrated. In the first place, there are certain primitive plants, such as the slime molds, which live but do not have cell walls. They consist of cell contents which have all grown together, and it is only when they produce their spores that the large mass of slime divides into individual cells, each with a cell wall around it. In some higher plants, too, we find stages in which cell contents are not separated into individual cells. But perhaps the best proof is that after the death of a plant its cell structure persists—in short, its walls remain, but the cell contents disappear.

The dynamic activities of a cell are most clearly expressed in the growing tip of a stem where very young cells will be found vigorously dividing. Because of its youth and activity, a young cell differs very much from a mature plant cell; in fact, it has many resemblances to an animal cell. It is small, about 1/2,000 of an inch in diameter, and is surrounded by a very thin cell wall. It is almost completely filled with protoplasm, the stuff that carries the life properties of the cell. Not only does it contain a virtually self-sufficient, self-operated chemical factory, it also contains all information necessary for its own reproduction, and even instructions as to what kind of a cell it will turn into: bark cell, leaf cell, root hair—any kind. It has its own power plant, its directors' and engineers' offices, its specialists and workmen. In addition it contains coded blueprints for the construction not only of another cell just like itself, but of a complete plant consisting of millions or billions of cells. Finally, it is its own construction company, its own toolmaker and its own troubleshooter, since it responds to demands put upon it by its environment.

T HOUGH it is indeed marvelous that so much can be packed into a single microscopic unit, it is, at the same time, clear that there is a minimal size for cells of higher plants below which not all operations can be carried out. This minimal size is apparently the size of the young dividing cell. For whether it be a large tree or a small weed, a complicated flowering plant or a simple moss, the dividing cells are always just about the same size, with the cells of the slow-growing plants somewhat larger than those of the fast-growing ones.

Much smaller than the cell itself is its central headquarters, the nucleus, a small round object that occupies less than 10 per cent of the internal volume of the young plant cell. During the last 50 years we have obtained conclusive evidence that the "information" for future development, the blueprints for growth, is contained in the nucleus, more specifically in the nucleic acids of the nucleus. The rest of the contents of the young cell consists mostly of cytoplasm, a proteinlike material which carries out all operations and produces and distributes the energy that powers the reactions and processes essential for the cell. It also obeys the signals and information distributed by the nucleus. We can therefore conclude that, just as in a modern factory, the greatest amount of space in the cell is taken up by the manufacturing departments, while the executive offices and central filing departments occupy only a small part of the whole.

In the very early stages of plant growth, in the embryo and at the very tip of a developing plant, growth is accomplished almost exclusively by division of the cells. Cells divide, as one might suspect, by forming a wall that runs approximately through the middle of the cell. However, the whole process is much more complicated than that. In the first place, there must be some provision for dividing up the contents of the cell evenly so that each half, after the division, will be a complete cell by itself. In the case of the protoplasm which fills the cell and of the many small bodies that float around in the protoplasm, this presents no problem, because normal division will ensure that approximately half of these things will find their way into each new cell. But the parent cell contains only one nucleus. Since the nucleus contains all the genetic information for future factory development, it is clear that its blueprints must be divided up in such a way that a complete set will be present in each new cell. If this is not done, the growth instructions to the new cells will be incomplete and they will not be able to develop normally. The duplication and separation mechanism of this genetic material is therefore of crucial importance for the continuation of the species. It is brought about by a process which, for all its extreme delicacy, is almost foolproof. We know this because deformities are the exception rather than the rule in cell division.

T HE process by which cell and nucleus divide is called mitosis. Investigators have managed to discover, by the use of dyes, what takes place within the nucleus to ensure that everything divides evenly. These dyes stain the nucleic acids inside the nucleus so that they can be seen. Ordinarily these nucleic acids are distributed at random throughout the nucleus, but just before mitosis starts they are assembled into long threads. These threads are the chromosomes, chains of genetic material on which are located the individual genes—the basic genetic units that will determine such specific characteristics as flower color, leaf shape, hairiness of stem, number of seeds and so on. Each gene has a very definite location on the chromosome thread, and each gene occurs only once on each chromosome. The crucial phases in mitosis, then, are (1) the duplication of each chromosome with all its genes and (2) the separation of these identical chromosomes to form two nuclei to be then separated by the new cell wall. This happens as follows: each chromosome divides lengthwise down its middle to produce an identical twin of itself. When this is done, the two sets of chromosomes gather at opposite ends, and the new cell wall which has been forming passes right between them, creating two complete cells, each with its own set of chromosomes reassembled into a nucleus. The chromosomes then seem to dissolve, but are ready, of course, to reassemble when the time comes for another cell division, at which point the whole process is repeated.

What proof is there that a single cell can hold within itself the blueprint for an entire plant? The best proof is supplied by a single fertilized egg, which by dividing over and over again will gradually change itself from a blob of undifferentiated cells into an embryo and finally into a complete plant. No one has yet been able to make the egg cell of a flowering plant develop outside its ovary, where this process can be observed from start to finish, but there is no doubt what happens. The fertilized egg of an oak—one cell—does eventually turn into a complete tree, that of a sunflower into a complete flower, that of a man into

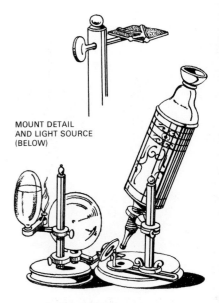

MOUNT DETAIL
AND LIGHT SOURCE
(BELOW)

ENLARGING THE VIEW

The English scientist Robert Hooke not only made the microscopic world familiar through his book "Micrographia" in 1665, but also improved the instruments for such studies. Shown here is Hooke's compound microscope with its elaborate light source—a reservoir-fed oil lamp, a water-filled globe to concentrate the lamplight and, finally, a lens next to the specimen mount to focus the light rays. In place on the mount (detail, top) is the bit of nettle leaf shown enlarged below.

STINGING NETTLE

The hollow needles and venom-filled sacs of a nettle plant (above) were sketched by Hooke, who tried their action on himself and compared them to bees' stings.

SHAPE AND FUNCTION

As a plant cell matures, it is modified according to the kind of work it is to perform. Eight types of cells, common to all higher plants, are shown on these pages.

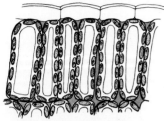

LIGHT CATCHERS

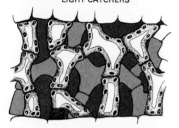

GAS EXCHANGERS

Oblong palisade cells (top), which perform photosynthesis, are lined up beneath the transparent upper surface layer of all leaves. Their light-responsive pigments lie inside many chloroplasts (black spots). Entirely different in shape are the spongy, irregular cells immediately beneath them. Surrounding large air channels, they absorb and give off gases in addition to their photosynthetic work.

WATERPROOFERS

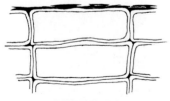

BARK FORMERS

The top and bottom surfaces of leaves are covered with a tough layer of close-knit epidermal cells (top) that manufacture a waxy, waterproof outer coat. In contrast, the outer skin of woody stems and branches is composed of cells which form cork (above) when they die. This air-filled layer may be inches thick, as in the cork oak, or paper thin, as in a potato skin.

a man. What is more, an oak egg cell *always* makes an oak and nothing else. It has never yet made a sunflower and never will. Obviously it has been responding to the blueprinted instructions inside itself.

So much for fertilized egg cells; there is evidence that other cells carry full sets of blueprints also. When a leaf is cut from a begonia plant and laid on moist sand in a greenhouse, a few of its cells will begin dividing at the place where it was cut. As the cell divisions continue, they will produce a sort of wart from which a complete new begonia plant will eventually develop. Although this happens very easily in begonias, nearly half of all other plants have this same marvelous ability. And not only will leaves or leaf stalks regenerate new plants; it can be done with pieces of stem or even bits of root.

Everything that we have so far described of the activities inside a dividing cell has been observed with a light microscope. However, this instrument is unable to see details smaller than 1/125,000 of an inch, because that is the wavelength of visible light. Anything smaller is necessarily invisible. In small dividing plant cells, therefore, the light microscope cannot see much detail. Such cells must be observed with a microscope using radiation of a much shorter wavelength—fast electrons, for example. These, in a typical electron microscope, have a wavelength 100 times shorter than light. Thus where the light microscope has to leave off, the electron miscroscope begins, and it is now generally used to see details which light microscopes cannot reveal. There is a major drawback, however; since an electron beam travels only in a vacuum, objects must be placed in a vacuum to be viewed, and no one has yet found a way of observing living cells under these conditions.

Protoplasm, which under the light microscope appears to be a clear, viscous liquid with a few objects in it, like the nucleus, plastids and mitochondria, looks very different when revealed in the electron beam. Suddenly we see that it is completely filled with small particles and everywhere crisscrossed with sheetlike bodies, far more complex in its structure than anyone had ever imagined.

As the newly divided plant cell becomes older, it stops dividing and starts to blow up like a balloon. This enlargement accounts for more than 90 per cent of the growth we observe. The cell absorbs a great deal of water, which collects in the small, so-called vacuoles in the center of the cell. This water, enriched with chemicals, is the cell sap. The protoplasm, whose volume usually remains unchanged during this inflation, is spread out more and more thinly against the cell walls by the expanding vacuoles, which by now have merged into one. In this type of growth by enlargement, plant cells are very different from animal cells, which grow exclusively by division and remain always filled with protoplasm. This is why animal cells—i.e., meat—are always high in protein. In plants, by contrast, only the young cells, such as wheat germ and nuts or growing shoots of bamboo and palm heart, are high in protein, whereas the adult cells are rich in sugars and minerals.

When it is first formed, a plant cell is covered with a thin and rather elastic cell wall which is capable of expansion as the cell enlarges. But as soon as the cell has reached its final size, the cell wall stiffens and, in many cases, thickens as new layers of wall material are deposited on the inside as it ages. The cell loses its flexibility completely, which is why young stems are pliable and older ones rigid and brittle. That also explains the tenderness of young carrots or string beans compared to old ones, and why the lower and older parts of the asparagus stem become tough and inedible.

The most extreme thickening of cell walls occurs in the woody part of stems and in fiber cells. The hardness of wood is entirely due to thickened cell walls, and the thicker they become the harder and the heavier the wood is. Wood with thin cell walls, such as balsa, is very light, but ironwood has so little air-filled cell space left between its extremely thick walls that it sinks in water. Cork is also a tissue with very thin but tough cell walls—so thin that they can even be compressed, which explains how corks can be forced into the necks of bottles.

Fibers are very long cells whose cell walls have also thickened with age. Cotton fibers are actually hairs which grow on the outside of cotton seeds, less than one inch long in short-staple cotton varieties but to a maximum of two and one half inches in the extra-long cotton grown in Egypt and the American Southwest. A cross section of a cotton fiber examined under a powerful microscope will reveal that its walls are built up in layers. It has been found that each layer corresponds to cell wall material deposited during one day. Since the thickness of each layer reflects the growing conditions during that day, a cotton fiber automatically keeps a record of the weather conditions of each of the days it grew.

W HAT role do cells play in the shape of a plant? An important one, determined partly by the shape of the cells themselves and partly by different cell arrangements. Most of the cells in a plant stem, for instance, are very long, sometimes 100 times longer than they are wide. On the other hand, most of the cells in a potato tuber, which is really just a monstrously thickened underground stem, are about as long as they are wide.

A plant's size is determined by the number of cells it has—a big plant has a large number of cells, small plants have relatively few. This means, too, that there is a limit to the smallness of a flowering plant; in any plant less than a fifth of an inch tall, there would not be enough cells to constitute proper leaves, stems, roots or flowers.

Though cells are rather uniform in size, they come in many shapes, and an easy way to see a large variety of these is to look at the hairs of plants. They may be long or short, spiny or club-shaped; they may be gland cells which excrete oil or digestive enzymes, or they may be absorptive, such as root hairs. When the cells are joined into tissues, the cell shapes are harder to recognize; then one has to make thin sections with a razor blade. From a large number of such sections, cut in different directions, the shapes of cells can be inferred.

A recently developed technique in botany, started less than 30 years ago, has thrown new light on our knowledge of plant cells. This is tissue culture. A tissue is a group of cells, usually all of one kind, which form a mass large enough to be seen with the naked eye. The tissue which has been cultivated most generally is callus tissue, an unorganized mass of large, more-or-less round cells which have no specific shape or function. This is the sort of tissue which normally forms on stems when they are wounded, like scar tissue on a cut finger. When a piece of stem is cut off, sterilized and placed in a glass tube containing nutrients, callus tissue will begin to form. If the culture is successful, a mass of tissue, irregularly shaped, will cover the exposed cut surface within a few weeks. This tissue can then be subcultured; that is to say, a small piece of it can be cut off, placed in a new tube with nutrients, and it in turn will start to grow, again in an unorganized fashion. Pieces thus cut off the callus can be subcultured indefinitely, provided certain substances—including plant hormones—are added in minute amounts to the culture medium.

During the last decade, cells from hundreds of plants have been grown in tis-

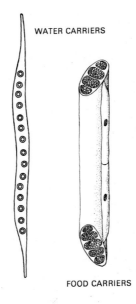

WATER CARRIERS

FOOD CARRIERS

A plant's circulatory system is twofold: one part transports water from root to leaf; the other carries dissolved sugars throughout the plant. Part of a water vessel is seen above (left). This cell forms one unit in a long pipeline of similar interconnected cells. A thick sieve tube cell, which moves food, is shown with a pair of slim companion cells (right). Sieve tube cells link end to end.

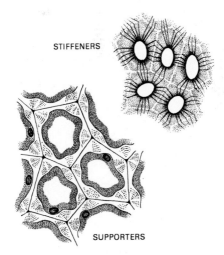

STIFFENERS

SUPPORTERS

Although the cellulose content of every cell wall adds something to the strength of a plant, some types of cells are specialized for rigidity. At left (above) are thick-walled "stone cells" of the sort that make up the shells of walnuts. At right are the long-lived, sturdy cells, called collenchyma, that furnish the supporting tissue in branches and stems.

sue culture, and no matter whether the cells are from a daisy, a tobacco or a carrot, the callus tissues all look pretty much alike. Yet they are *not* the same. For occasionally a few cells of such a callus tissue will begin to differentiate and ultimately grow into complete plants. When they do, the carrot callus produces a perfectly normal and typical carrot plant, and the callus of a tobacco produces a tobacco plant.

Even more recently investigators have succeeded in taking a single cell from a tissue culture, growing it into a large callus and then producing an entire plant from this callus. Here is complete proof that not only is a fertilized egg cell capable of reproducing an entire plant, but that an ordinary tissue cell can do the same. This is the final vindication of the cell theory enunciated by Schleiden and Schwann a century and a quarter ago.

From all these experiments it follows that a plant is built up from cells which are put together according to a very specific plan. They can be compared to a pile of bricks and stones: looked at individually or as a pile, they reveal nothing about whether they will be used to build a cathedral or a jail. In the same way, one cannot tell whether a mass of cells will produce a carrot or a tobacco plant; yet the architectural plan within each cell will invariably see to it that it produces what it is supposed to.

T HE cellular architecture of plants is pretty well known. Plant anatomists, who study cell structure, have described in detail how leaves, stems and roots are put together. Simply by looking at a piece of wood under a microscope, experts can tell the kind of tree it was cut from, for each plant has its own special arrangement of cells or its own types of cells. In the same way it is possible to determine whether the filling of a cigarette is real dried tobacco leaves or whether tea has been adulterated with other leaves.

Although it is easy enough to recognize the arrangement of wood, bark and cork cells, we have no idea as yet how these arrangements take place in the growing plant or even how the various cells assume their specific shapes. Yet there are a few clues along the way, pointing toward an explanation.

When we try to grow a small piece of a plant root in a culture medium in the way we grow callus tissues, we find that this is possible provided the piece of root is long enough. If we cut off too short a piece—only 1/25 of an inch, say—we get not a root but an undifferentiated callus culture. On the other hand, a piece two or three times as long will continue to grow as a root. Clearly, therefore, a piece of root which has already begun to be differentiated as a root must be present to make new cells assume the configuration of roots.

This may seem to contradict something we learned earlier in this chapter. If a bit of root has to be more than a certain minimum size, how is it that a *single* egg cell, much smaller than a bit of root, can grow into a complete plant instead of into a mere blob of cells like a callus? This is made more mysterious by the fact that in its earliest growth stages the egg cell *does* grow into a blob of undifferentiated cells like a callus. However, as it stays in the ovary of the mother plant, it eventually is transformed into an embryo plant itself, complete with seedling leaves and rootlet. The only conclusion that can be drawn from this is that the infant plant's presence inside its mother's ovary is important—that this presence manages in some way to aid it in its transformation from blob to seed.

However, this is not the whole story, as orchids will quickly show. A ripe orchid seed is still just a blob of undifferentiated cells when it is carried away from the mother plant by the wind. If it lands in a place where it can germinate

—or if it is grown in a test tube—it will start to enlarge. Still it does not differentiate. It may remain a blob until it is as much as 1/15 of an inch in diameter, and all the time it will look exactly like a piece of callus tissue. Then, for some unknown reason, a tiny leaflet and rootlet will sprout in a particular spot, and from these a normal orchid plant will develop.

As we have seen, this is very much like what occasionally happens in callus cultures. Certain cells at certain times may transform into leaf, stem or root cells anywhere on the callus tissue. Once this has happened, a complete plant can form. Perhaps this is connected with the balance of certain growth substances, such as kinetin, which seem to influence many of the same processes as the plant hormones, but this we do not yet know. The specific reasons for this differentiation remain utterly obscure. We find much the same problem in the forces that control the development of a mushroom on the threadlike growths, or hyphae, of a fungus. In culture flasks we can produce a dense cover of these hyphae without ever obtaining the mushroom—which is actually the fruiting body of the fungus. Sometimes, if we place a small twig in the flask, a mushroom will develop on it, but this is never certain. Mushrooms are extremely capricious, and some of the most delicious types which are collected in the wild can never be cultivated: we just do not know how to make mushrooms develop on the mass of hyphae in the culture bed. There is only one kind of cultivated mushroom that people in the Western world can buy in their markets. This is the *Agaricus campestris*, which consistently produces fruiting bodies on a culture medium. In Java, a mushroom named *Volvaria* is sold by vendors along the street; this particular species can be grown only on rice straw.

The very specialized conditions which cause the formation of mushrooms on their hyphae may be responsible for the irregularity with which mushrooms are found in nature. Whereas the humus layer of the forest floor is always riddled with the hyphae of fungi, there are seldom many mushrooms, and in certain years there may be almost none.

IT remains now to be said that in the plant body there is a strict division of labor between the various kinds of cells. Some, filled with chloroplasts, have the job of carrying out the vital process of photosynthesis, transforming energy from light into the chemical energy the plant needs—these occur in the leaves. Others, as we have seen, perform various functions in roots and stem. Among the most interesting are those which constitute the vessels through which the plant moves water from the roots throughout its system, and the sieve tubes which carry sugar from the photosynthesizing leaves.

The first microscopist who looked at these water-transporting vessels in wood saw in them a resemblance to our own windpipe, or trachea, and they have suffered from a misnomer ever since. The human windpipe is prevented from collapsing by rings of cartilage reinforcing the walls; the water vessels in wood have similar reinforcements, so they were called tracheae in the belief that they, too, served to supply air. Actually, they do not carry air at all, but only water and the nutrients which are dissolved in it and which the plant needs—they make up the plumbing system which we shall read about in a later chapter. For the moment, however, we are concerned only with how these tubes are formed from the plant cells.

In their finished form, the wood tracheae, or water vessels, are tubes which on the average are about a foot in length but may be a yard or more, with a diameter up to 1/25 of an inch. Each of them, therefore, is thousands of times longer than any ordinary cell, and for a long time it was thought that they constituted the exception to the rule of the cell theory, which says that all components of a plant are either cells or derived from cells.

However, when we observe the early stages of development of such a tube, we find that it does not start as a tube at all, but as a series of cells, one above the other, all of which have the same diameter. As the vessel matures, the cell walls between the stacked cells dissolve and they merge at last into one long tube. Finally, all the living contents of the cells—the cytoplasm, nucleus and other bodies—disappear, leaving only water in the tube.

Obviously, it takes a great many cells to make up one such tube—since the average stem cell is less than 1/25 of an inch in length, a one-yard vessel requires the merging of about 1,000 cells. Any plant, from a small flower to a towering tree, will have any number of these tubes stacked in bundles and running to whatever height may be required. It is easy to determine how long each separate tube in a stem or branch may be: you simply connect a length of it to a faucet with a rubber tube, turn on the water and watch to see if it drips out. If it does not, you cut off small pieces of the length until it does. When water begins to ooze out of the end, you will have found the approximate length of the longest vessel. In a big climbing vine like a tropical liana this may be up to several yards, in trees perhaps a yard or less, in shrubs and herbs less than a foot.

Since in each separate length of tube the cross walls have dissolved, it is easy enough to see how water can flow through a single tube; but how does it get from vessel to vessel in a stack which may be as high as a tall tree? The answer can be found by looking at the cell walls between the vessels. It will be seen that they are not of a uniform thickness; rather, they have a series of near perforations which look like tiny pits. In each such pit the cell wall is ultra-thin, a water-permeable membrane stretched between the thick parts of the wall. There are enough of these pits to assure that all the bundled-together tubes can exchange water through their sides and function together as a single tube.

However, water is not the only substance which has to be moved over long distances in a plant; sugar has to be carried in the opposite direction, down from the leaves. Clearly, the water-carrying tubes cannot be used for this purpose; they cannot accommodate two-way traffic, and furthermore, since they have no protoplasm in them which keeps the sugar contained in living cells, the sugar would ooze out.

For this reason, plants have to produce a different kind of tube to carry sugar from the leaves to all the cells that need it, like those of the stem, roots, flowers and fruits. This they do in the form of sieve tubes, but in this case, tubes formed of living cells in the bark. The sugar streams from one tube to another through a cell wall perforated with tiny pores constituting the sieve plate. This sieve plate, furthermore, acts as a valve to control the flow of sugar: if the stream is too fast, the pores plug up. Thus the plant cannot "bleed to death" if the bark is cut or bruised. In fact, the only way this sugar can be tapped is by aphids, those tiny insects which feed on the sugar in plants and trees. They are able to drill into an individual sieve tube with their mouths, and the sap then streams into them—the aphids, in effect, tap a gusher. When their bodies are filled with sugar, the excess oozes out, and this produces the sticky cover that people often find to their sorrow on cars which they have parked under aphid-infested trees.

UNDER POLARIZED LIGHT, SOME OF THE MANY, USUALLY COLORLESS CRYSTALS FORMED BY AN ONIONSKIN CELL GLOW PINK AND YELLOW

A Microscopic Workshop

The cell is the smallest living unit of the plant. It not only reproduces itself, but also designs and organizes the tissues that will provide framework, water and food supply, storage and protective outer covering. These basic units make up all the various kinds of plants, following in each case the unique internal patterns that will result in a pine needle or a grass blade, a mushroom or an oak.

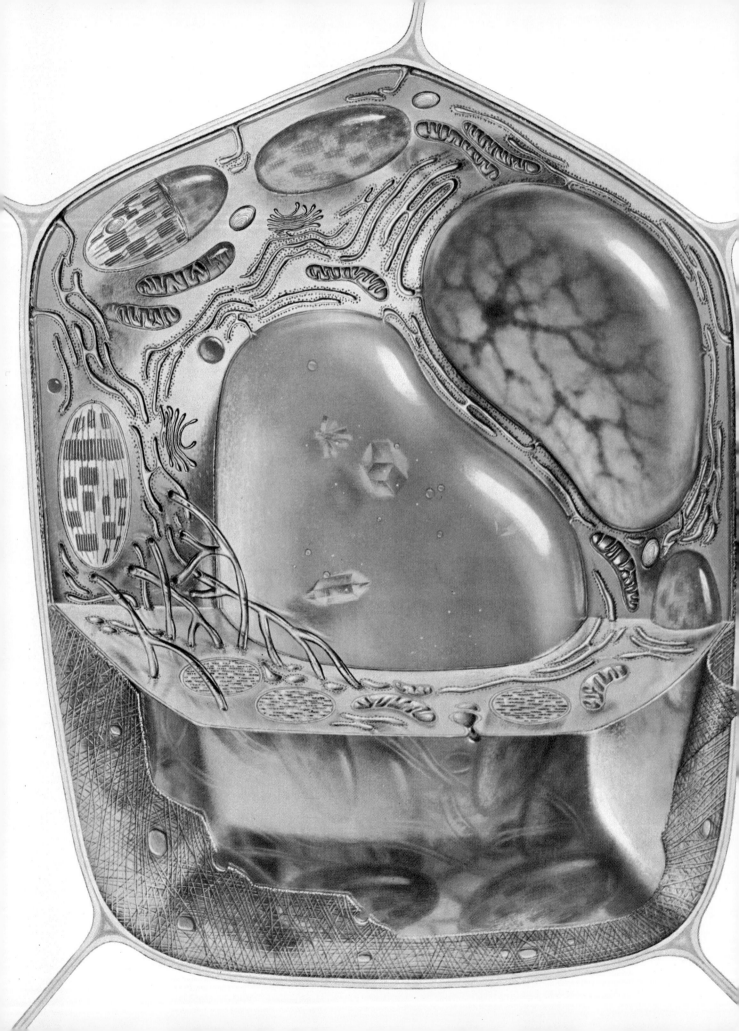

The Anatomy of a Plant Cell

All plant or animal cells fall basically into two parts: the nucleus, or control center, and the cytoplasm, which includes all the other bodies suspended in the protoplasm of the cell. In plants, however, the cytoplasm carries some bodies that are quite different from an animal cell. There are, for instance, the plastids, varying in shape and size, some of them containing the green chlorophyll essential to photo-synthesis, others with carotene pigments for differ-ent functions (*see below*). The vacuole, large and centralized in a maturing cell like the one shown here, swells up with cell sap as the cell matures, stretching the flexible walls. Throughout, cell ma-terials are exchanged through pits in the walls into those of neighboring cells, and the whole protoplasm with all its bodies is in constant streaming motion.

THE NUCLEUS in its permeable membrane contains two types of nucleic acid molecules, deoxyribonucleic acid, or DNA, and ribo-nucleic acid, or RNA. These determine what a plant will be. DNA, in the chromosomes, embodies the genetic code. Between cell di-visions, DNA reproduces itself. Its informa-tion goes to RNA, which migrates to the small, round nucleolus. From there it passes to the cytoplasm and dictates all cell functions.

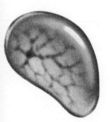

THE MITOCHONDRIA are the energy organ-elles of the cell. They contain proteins and are literally "powerhouses," oxidizing food and converting energy to adenosine triphosphate, or ATP, the agent in many reactions, includ-ing enzyme synthesis. They are filled with accordionlike inner membranes which increase the surface on which reactions can take place.

THE CHLOROPLASTS are the largest bodies in the cytoplasm. Developing in stem and, par-ticularly, leaf cells, they contain green pigment which, in photosynthesis, absorbs the sun's energy and uses it to convert carbon dioxide into sugar, the plant's source of chemical en-ergy and food. Chloroplasts multiply by split-ting independently of the nuclear division.

CAROTENE CHROMOPLASTS lend the charac-teristic color to plants like carrots and toma-toes, ripe peppers, citrus fruits and the petals of many flowers. They come in several colors, from yellow to deep red; their actual chemical functions in the plant are largely unknown.

THE GOLGI STRUCTURES, which are bundles of tiny vessels that are made up of fats and proteins, may act as some sort of chemical storehouse for the cell. Various enzymes and other substances collect and presumably con-dense on their surface. When the rate of me-tabolism increases, the structures enlarge, but their precise role in plants is still unclear.

THE ENDOPLASMIC RETICULUM is a network of small platelets spreading loosely between membranes throughout the cytoplasm to pro-vide channels for the passage of materials. Usually associated with it are the ribosomes (red dots), composed of protein and the nu-cleic acid, RNA. These particles, which syn-thesize proteins, receive instructions via RNA.

STARCH GRAINS are the storage bins in which the plant keeps its reserve supplies of food. Made up of crystalline layers of carbohydrates, these grains vary in shape according to the spe-cies of plant. Most of the starch accumulates in mature tissues, in stems, tubers and fruits.

CELL WALLS are thin, multilayered and, in their early stages, flexible. The basic layer, formed at the time of cell division, is primarily pectin, the familiar substance that makes jelly "jell." Thus it is responsible for cementing neighboring cells together. After cell division, each one of the new daughter cells builds an inner wall of cellulose fibrils, which expands as the cell grows. Eventually, in the mature plant, the walls become thick and inflexible.

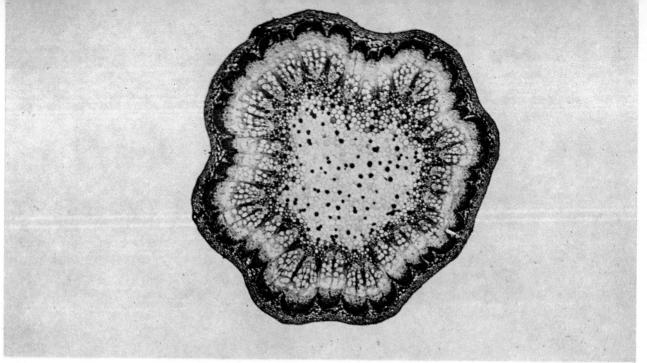

A YOUNG SYCAMORE, a typical dicot *(above)*, has built a ring of woody tissue with transport vessels around its pith core.

AN OLDER SYCAMORE *(below)* shows years of growth rings which had added to its girth. Pith rays traverse it radially.

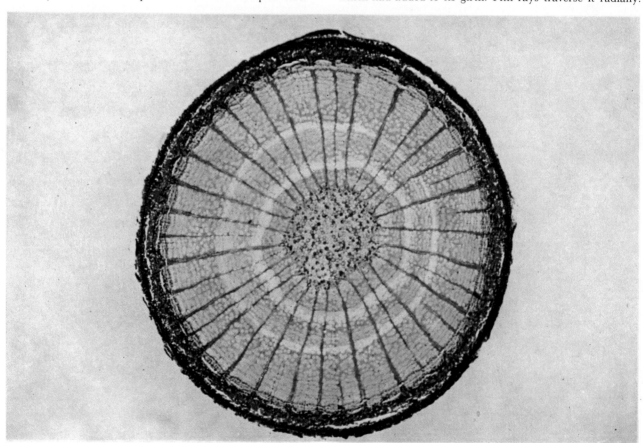

Architecture and Plumbing in the Stems

In the complex process of forming a plant, growing cells follow a precise architectural plan. The two broad groups of flowering plants, the dicots and monocots, show this in striking fashion in the entirely different structure of their stems and the

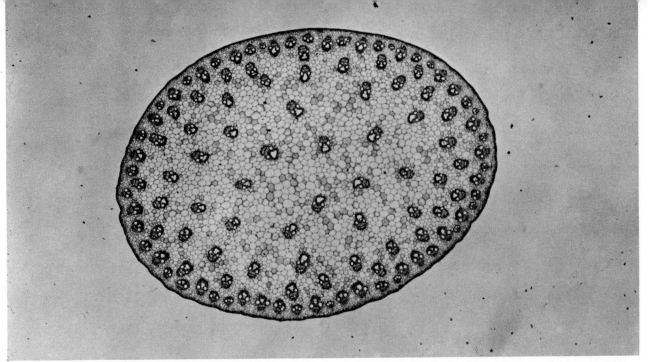

A YOUNG CORN STEM, a typical monocot (*above*), has no central core. Its bundles are scattered at random in the stem tissue.

AN OLDER CORN STEM (*below*), though it is some weeks further along, shows precisely the same type of vascular structure.

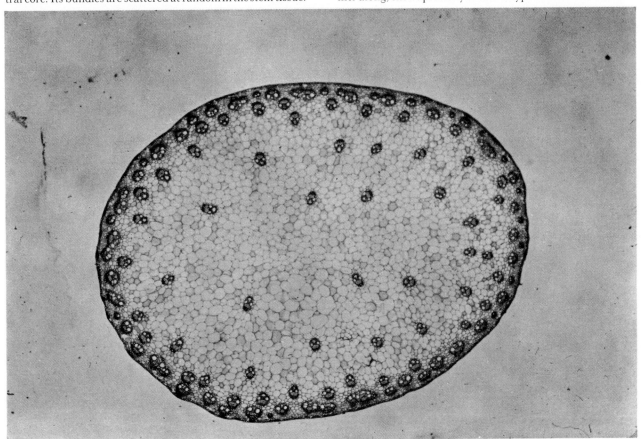

plumbing system which keeps them supplied with water and nutrients. In dicots, which include such diverse species as buttercups, poppies and many hardwood trees, their stems thicken by cell division, adding woody rings around a central core. Water and food vessels are formed between rays of pith as the plant matures. Most monocots follow no such concentric plan: their stems increase in diameter by cell enlargement. The bundles of vessels are spread randomly through relatively soft tissue.

47

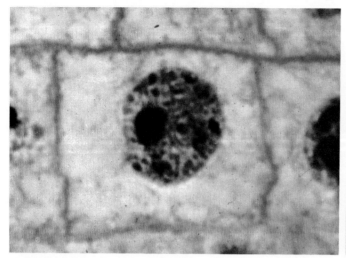

1 Just before division, the nucleus of an onion root-tip cell shows a clump of fine threads, the gene-bearing chromosomes.

2 At the start of mitosis, the chromosomes have duplicated themselves, molecule for molecule, and now lie in loose coils.

Mitosis: A Cell Division

Most of the growth of plants is accounted for by the simple swelling up and elongation of the cells as they absorb water piped up from the roots. But in certain areas, such as the tips of developing stems and roots, they grow through an increase of cells brought about by cell division. How this process, called mitosis, is accomplished is shown here.

Cell division may be triggered by an increase in the amount of cytoplasm coupled with the synthesis of certain chemicals, or by chemical action without previous growth. During this preparatory period, the nucleus is large and the chromosomal material is reproduced, molecule for molecule, with all its genes. Coming together as threads, the chromosomes then condense to compact bodies and mitosis begins. The final phase, after the doubled chromosomes have separated and formed two new, complete nuclei, occurs when a cell membrane, or plate, divides the cytoplasm approximately in half, forming two daughter cells, which inherit the complete plan for the further organization and growth of the plant. Mitosis lasts from one half to two hours, depending on the species of plant, and is eventually followed by further growth and division. Two cells produce four, and four produce eight, in increasing multiples of thin-walled building blocks. As the plant reaches maturity, however, cell division gradually slows down until it continues only in specialized tissues of roots, stem, leaves and reproductive organs.

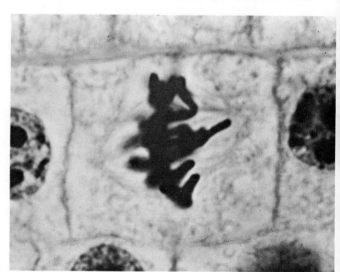

5 At the end of a minute, each chromatid appears attached to one of the spindle fibers and the twin bodies start to separate.

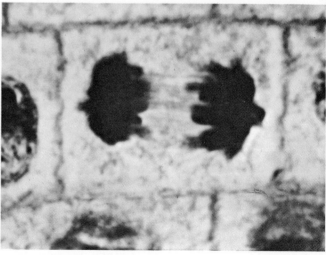

8 Within two to three minutes, the long fibers of the spindle have begun to disintegrate and the new nuclei take shape.

48

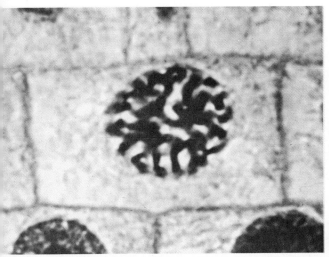

3 About an hour later, the coiled halves, or chromatids, have condensed and the rest of the nucleus has dissolved.

4 Now almost invisible fibers have formed from opposite poles of the cell, and the chromatids are aligning at the center.

6 Now the fibers shorten and the chromatids move apart, following the spindle pathway toward opposite poles of the cell.

7 After their migration to opposite poles, the chromatids are separate, independent chromosomes, complete with genes.

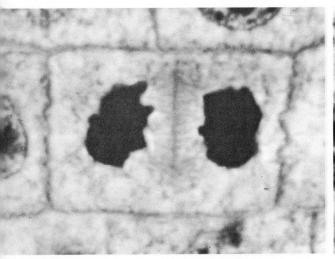

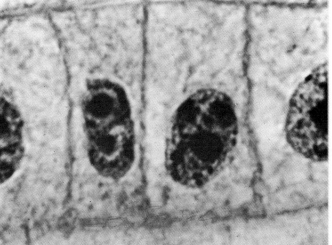

9 In the remaining four minutes, a fluid membrane known as the cell plate begins to develop, separating the new nuclei.

10 Growing outward to the walls of the original root-tip cell, the new wall completes the division of the two daughter cells.

HARD: SILVER MAPLE

Hardwood and Softwood

Many of the slow-growing deciduous trees, such as the maple and the oak, have harder and stronger wood than the faster-growing conifers. This has led to their being called hardwoods, as opposed to the softwood conifers. Actually, hardness or softness is not a consistent characteristic of either. The only really consistent difference between the two groups is structural, deriving from the nature of the sap-transporting vessels and pith rays. In these microphotographs of a hardwood silver maple tree and a softwood pitch pine, this difference in cellular structure and texture becomes immediately apparent.

SOFT: PITCH PINE

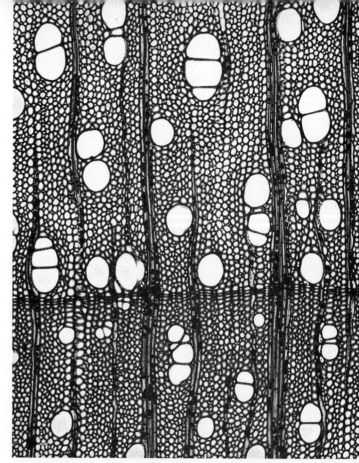

CROSS SECTION of hardwood shows many large vessels formed from stacks of open-end cells. The dark vertical lines are pith rays.

CROSS SECTION of softwood shows a close-knit mesh of cells separated by pith rays, some with the large ducts that carry resin.

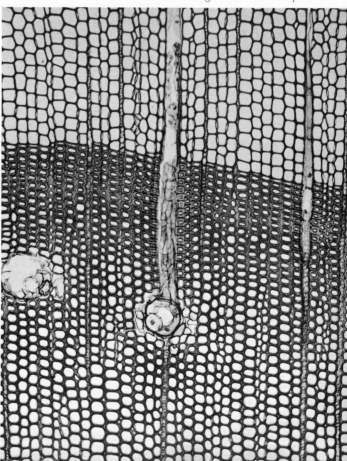

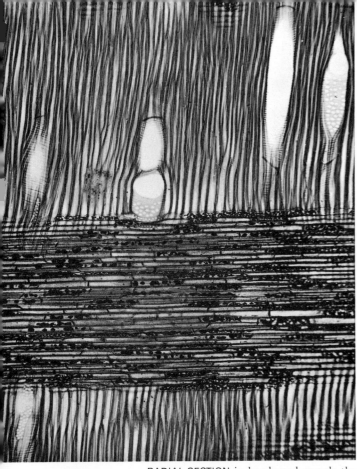

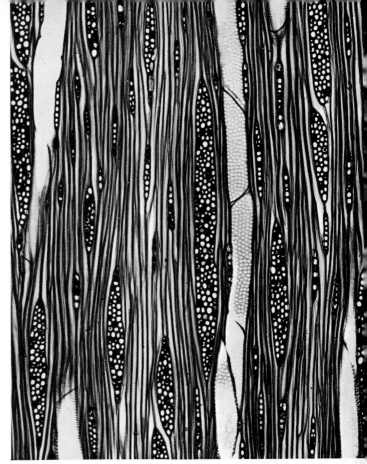

RADIAL SECTION in hardwood reveals the length of water-transporting vessels and height of the pith ray running crosswise.

RADIAL SECTION in softwood shows lines of the parallel, pitted, water-carrying cells intersected by islands of dark pith rays.

TANGENTIAL CUT in hardwood shows the rays head on as dark areas flecked with the white dots indicating food-transport cells.

TANGENTIAL CUT in softwood reveals its lengthwise pattern. Water-transport cells lie between rays with their bundled ducts.

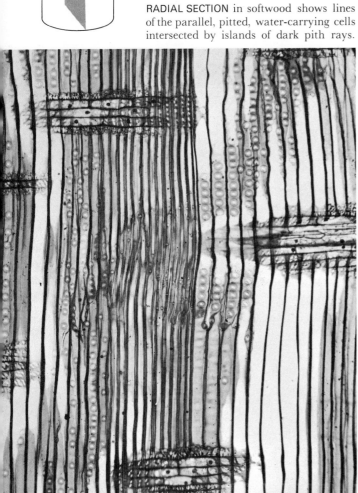

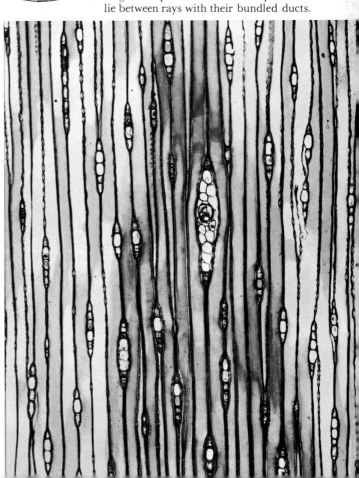

A PINE NEEDLE SPRAY is made up of two or more triangular leaves arranged in bundles on a short spur shoot. The entire shoot is eventually shed.

A Leaf in a Needle

Unlike the advanced flowering trees, which have evolved broad leaves with profusely branching veins, most of the more primitive conifers have never gone beyond their simple and efficient cluster of needles, each one a unit in itself, which convert carbon dioxide into sugar that will nourish the plant. The triangular pine needle shown here is over four inches long but only 1/16 of an inch wide. It has a single vein in the center, containing the tracheids that bring water and nutrients to the leaf, and the sieve tubes that transport dissolved sugar to other parts. Outside of this central core are a tissue of food-producing cells, the mesophyll, and the wound-healing resin ducts, all enclosed in a porous but very hard covering. Small, compact and thick-walled, needles are well adapted to endure a variety of climates, from the tropics to the timber line or even polar regions. Some shoots are shed each year, but they usually stay on the tree until new needles are fully grown.

A CROSS SECTION OF A NEEDLE shows its compact structure (*right*). The vein is set in the center of mesophyll cells, bounded by a hard, porous covering. The ducts at top carry resin.

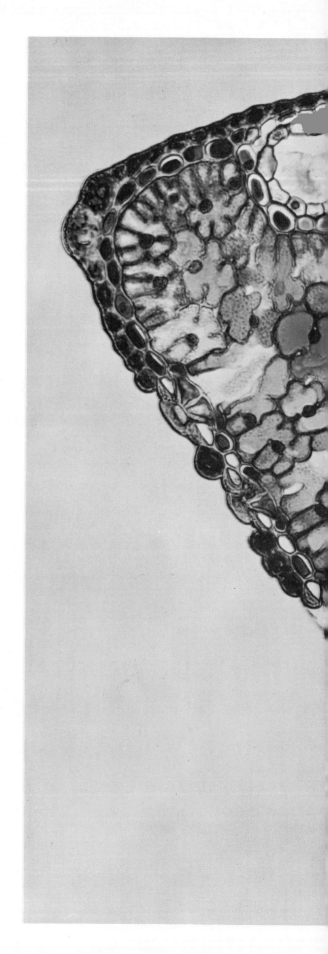

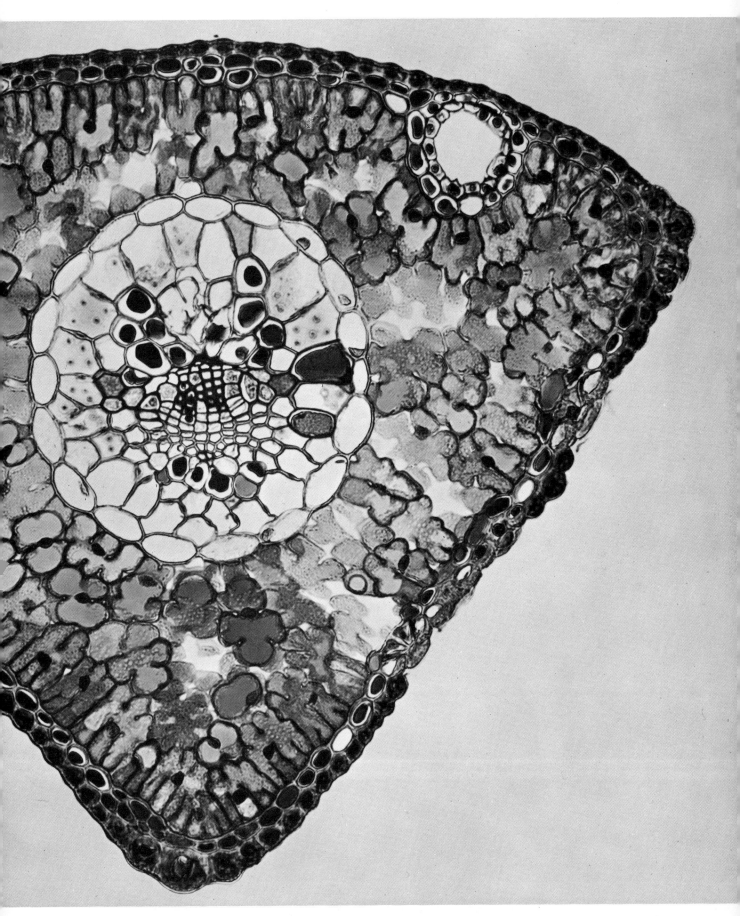

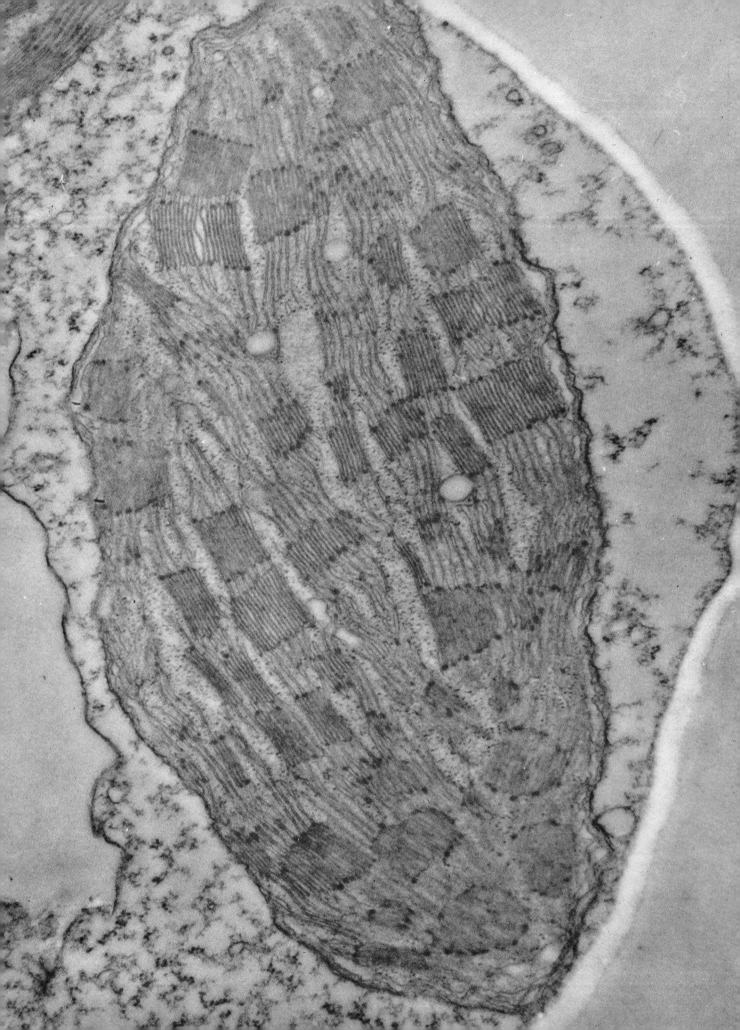

3

The Plant

as a

Chemical Factory

WHAT makes plants tick? We have seen in the previous chapter that they are made up of cells, and with the aid of the light and electron microscopes we can examine these cells in detail. But if we want to find out how they function, what they do, we have to get down to the molecular level, where chemical reactions occur. Since molecules are in the size range of angstrom units—one ten thousandth of a micron, or four one-billionths of an inch—it is obvious that at this level we cannot see what goes on in the cell. We can only deduce this from chemical information—and there, working amidst the infinitely small, we find ourselves involved in some of the most fascinating processes in nature.

Tiny though it may be, a cell is really a complete chemical factory of incredible complexity. It contains thousands of compounds and continuously produces hundreds of substances which form part of the chain of reactions which keep it in operation. Two hundred years ago, we would have been able to learn almost nothing about all these activities; chemistry simply had not progressed far enough to give us the necessary tools for discovering and recording them. But since 1828, with the inception of the chemistry of biological materials—or organic chemistry, to give it its proper name—many of the details of the molec-

ANALYZING THE PLANTS

A precise way to identify the different chemicals that plants produce is chromatographic analysis, a system that separates organic compounds. Four kinds of chromatography are seen on these pages.

COLUMN

Plant pigments are separated by column chromatography. The dissolved pigment flows down a column packed with an adsorbent such as chalk. Different pigment components travel at different speeds and form bands (enlargement). These may be drained off separately (tubes, above) or, when a gel is used, sliced off for analysis.

PAPER

Plant sugars and acids are separated by paper chromatography. The material under study is applied in solution to the top of a piece of paper, which is suspended from a dish of solvent in a closed, humid container. As the paper blots up the solvent, the test solution diffuses and its different components are separated in bands.

ular world have been laid bare, much as the light microscope and the electron microscope have revealed the world which lies beyond the range of the naked eye. Organic chemistry has had a tremendous impact on biology, and conversely, biology by its advances has greatly stimulated chemistry. Researchers who study the functioning of plants have benefited from both.

At the basis of all the chemical activities of the cell is respiration. When we hear this word, we think of breathing—the mechanical business of inhaling and exhaling. But in a general biological sense, respiration is a chemical rather than a mechanical process. It is, in fact, a complex of reactions within the cell, which results in the release of energy from food. So when we talk of respiration in this chapter, we are talking about the oxidation of food, which provides the energy that plants need to live and grow.

Now let us tool up our private chemical laboratory—our tongue, our nose and our eyes—and see what we can learn about the chemistry of the cell. To start with we will use taste and smell to separate some of the substances we are examining. There are water-soluble chemicals in cells, like sugar and salt, that have no odor at all, but which have a strong taste; whereas others like perfume, turpentine and camphor do not need to be tasted because they are volatile, spreading their substance into the air, molecule by molecule, and thus recognizable to the nose as smells.

The first subject of our examination will be an unripe apple. One bite taken from such an apple will reveal that it is hard and sour. Sourness indicates the presence of an acid—and indeed unripe apples are full of acid, but what kind? Smelling the apple, the next step, will partially answer the question—it will immediately eliminate a whole group of volatile acids like formic, acetic and butyric acid, all of which sting and burn the nose. An unripe apple, save for a very faint "apple" smell, has no aroma at all, indicating that the acids present are of the nonvolatile kind, like malic or citric acid, commonly found in fruit. Meanwhile, what about that astringent taste of the apple's skin? That comes from tannic acid, which reacts with the proteins on the surface of the tongue to give the familiar sensation of puckering.

All of these acids have their specific functions in the chemical factory contained within the plant cell. For the moment, it is sufficient for our purposes to note that they are there in the unripe apple. What they contribute to the ripening process, which is to say the maturing of the fruit, will be discussed in more detail at a later stage.

Now let us go on to examine an apple that *has* ripened. First of all, we find the taste has greatly changed. Instead of being acid and astringent, it has turned sweet; the cells have become filled with sugar. Furthermore, the apple is aromatic—it has a distinct fruity smell (which, incidentally, is a good test of ripeness in any fruit). Since it does not smell of pine or eucalyptus, we know that its aroma is not due to terpenes, the turpentinelike substances characteristic of such trees. It comes, instead, from chemical compounds called esters, which are formed by a combination of an acid, such as we found in the unripe apple, and an alcohol. Most simple esters are very volatile and very aromatic, and their presence in the apple at this stage tells us a good deal about what has been going on inside the cells while the apple was ripening.

We have established, simply by tasting, that the acids in the ripened apple have mostly disappeared and have been replaced by sugars and esters. But why are the sugars there? Partly they are useful in tempting animals to eat them and thus distribute the seeds, but in addition they are needed for energy use by the apple. Here we begin to get to the heart of the matter. Sugar, when it combines with oxygen, will produce chemical energy which can be used for growth and for the formation of other chemicals needed to sustain life. In chemical terms, sugar plus oxygen produces chemical energy, along with carbon dioxide and water. This is respiration—food reacting with oxygen to produce energy. To explain this in terms of the chemical elements involved, chemists write the formula as follows (with C standing for carbon, H for hydrogen, O for oxygen, and the relative amounts of each expressed in numbers):

$$C_6H_{12}O_6 + 6O_2 \rightarrow 6CO_2 + 6H_2O + \text{chemical energy}$$

—or, in ordinary language: a sugar molecule reacting with six oxygen molecules makes six carbon dioxide molecules and six water molecules, and releases energy in addition.

This is an over-all formula covering many complex processes taking place inside the cell and involving many of the substances we have identified, but it is the basic formula—and we will meet it in surprising fashion later, when we learn how plants manufacture some of their own energy from sunlight.

So much for the sugar. Now, where did the esters come from and what is their function? This brings us to a different form of respiration, one in which oxygen is not present in sufficient amounts to produce the reaction above—as, for instance, in the center of the apple. This respiration without oxygen is called anaerobic respiration, and it breaks down the sugar without the benefit of air to release chemical energy. This time it produces carbon dioxide and alcohol. The alcohol, as we have seen, combines with the acids in the cell to form the esters that give the ripening apple its characteristic fruity aroma.

Now let us go one step further and examine an apple that is overripe. The first thing we notice is that it has become mealy and has lost its taste: the sugars and the acids seem to have disappeared, though it still has an aromatic smell. It is up to us now to find a reason why the apple no longer tastes good, although it still smells good, so we will move our experiment into the kitchen.

Here we cut the apple into small pieces and boil it in a little water. The result is a sort of mush—but lo and behold (or rather lo and taste), the mush, or applesauce, which we produced by cooking, is full of flavor: sweet, tart and aromatic. Clearly, the sugars and acids of the ripe apple were still there in the overripe one, but why did we not taste them when we bit into the apple?

T HE answer lies in the apple's mealiness, and it gives us still further clues about other cellular processes inside the apple. Under the microscope we would see that the cells of the overripe apple have begun to separate from each other. Each cell is still intact, but it is no longer firmly attached to its neighboring cells. The result is that instead of being forcibly broken apart by chewing, which would release the cell sap in a firm, ripe apple, the cells in the overripe apple detach themselves easily from each other and escape between our teeth, each cell intact, with its load of cell sap undisturbed. Only when we cook the cells and kill them is the cell sap set free with all its acids, sugars and aromatic esters.

From this we learn that during the latter part of the ripening process no further changes occur on the *inside* of the apple cells, but things do begin to happen on their outside—to the cell walls. The wall of a young cell consists of a rather flexible substance called protopectin, against which a much tougher cellulose wall is laid down. In the unripe apple the protopectin holds the cellulose walls together, but upon ripening, an enzyme is produced which dissolves the

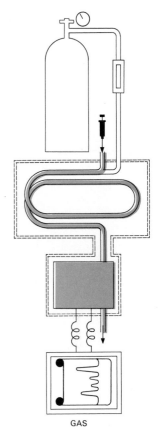

Plant oils are separated by gas chromatography. The oil sample is injected into a pressurized stream of gas that passes through a pipe containing an adsorbent. The adsorbent helps to separate the mixture. Each component of the sample then passes into a detector unit and its type and quantity are recorded on a graph.

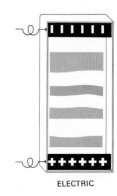

ELECTRIC

Plant proteins are separated by electrophoresis. The protein is first dissolved and then applied to the center of a strip of wet paper (dark line above). When an electric current passes through the paper, the sample separates into bands, as positive and negative particles move toward the two poles at different rates of speed.

protopectin and changes it into pectin. This releases the individual cells so that the apple turns soft and mealy. The pectin thus set free will jell when boiled with sugar, and there we have fruit jellies. While this is going on, acids inside the cells have combined with the alcohol formed by anaerobic respiration to form the aromatic esters—and the riper the apple gets the stronger and more aromatic it smells.

It is interesting to follow up these apple experiments with some observations on really large fruits, such as melons and pineapples. The larger the fruit, the less oxygen there will be at its center, and the more alcohol will be formed by anaerobic respiration. Consequently it is not surprising that melons and pineapples are among the most aromatic of all fruits; they produce so many alcohols that their ester content is higher than that of most smaller fruits.

Alcohol leads naturally to the subject of wine and grapes. A quick test with nose and tongue will reveal that ripe grapes contain a great deal of sugar and some fruit acids, but relatively few aromatic substances—they do not smell as strongly as ripe apples. From this we may deduce that they contain little alcohol. And so it is—when grapes are pressed and their juice is put in vats, certain yeasts must be added, so that in the resulting fermentation of their sugars, alcohol will be formed. This alcohol can now combine with the fruit acids in the juice, and this is the start of the aromatic flavor of wine, which the grapes themselves did not have. Since each kind of grape contains different fruit acids, and each yeast produces different alcohols, a large number of different wines exist, each with its own particular flavor.

WE can squeeze still more chemical information from ripening fruit, but this time we will use our eyes as test tools, by observing the color changes. These again give us important clues to what happens inside the cell. The appearance and disappearance of colored substances, or pigments, can easily be seen. But we must remember that one color can mask another, as a yellow pigment is masked by blue when both together produce green. This happens in leaves, where the yellow carotenoid pigments are usually masked by the bluish-green chlorophylls, producing a light green. Depending upon the proportion of carotenoids and chlorophylls, leaves may look anywhere from yellowish green to dark green, with all possible gradations between them.

Most fruits are green when unripe, meaning they contain a lot of chlorophyll. Some varieties of apples remain green even when fully ripe, others turn a soft yellow, and still others turn red. The yellowing of apples is at least partly due to the disappearance of the masking green of chlorophyll, permitting the carotenoid pigments in the cells of the skin to proclaim their color. The carotenoids are chemically more stable than chlorophyll, sugar, tannin or most other chemical constituents and therefore are often the last chemicals to stay. But whereas the yellow color of ripening apples is not due to a new pigment, the red color is. It is caused by an anthocyanin, closely related to the red colors of geranium or poppy petals, and its appearance gives us still further details about chemicals in the cell.

Unlike the carotenoids and chlorophylls, which are located in the plastids inside the cell, the anthocyanins are dissolved directly in the cell sap. They can be extracted by boiling a piece of apple skin. As the water boils, the red color of the skin begins to disappear, first along the edges of the peeling and finally in its center. This loss of color indicates the gradual loss of anthocyanin, which is released from the individual cells, along with the cell sap, when the cells are broken down by boiling. Even though the water in which the apple skin was boiled may seem colorless, anthocyanin is present, and this can be checked by pouring some vinegar or other acid into the water. It will immediately turn pink. Further similar experiments will reveal that many anthocyanins turn pink or red in the presence of an acid. And, since this anthocyanin is red when dissolved in cell sap, we can conclude that cell sap is acid.

It is not news, of course, that apple cells contain acid; we have already determined that with our tongues. What is significant is that we have now pinpointed the location of the acid—in the cell sap. And from this one fragment of knowledge we can take gradual steps forward in the unraveling of the interior construction of the cell, working always in the invisible world of the submicroscopic, with only the clues supplied by chemical reactions as our guide.

A second step can be supplied by cooking another piece of apple skin and watching the process more closely. Drop this second bit of skin into boiling water; it will be seen to turn from red to purple before the color fades away. Since alkalinity turns anthocyanins purple just as acids turn them red, it is clear that the anthocyanin in the apple skin encountered an alkali momentarily during the breakdown of the cell by boiling. The other major ingredient of a cell is protoplasm, so this indicates that protoplasm is slightly alkaline. It also follows that within the living cell there must be some kind of barrier that keeps the slightly acid cell sap separated from the slightly alkaline protoplasm. From such simple but astute observations much of the intricate internal structure of cells has been learned.

About the same processes which occur in ripening fruits take place in leaves in the fall. The yellowing of cottonwood leaves, for instance, is mainly due to a disappearance of chlorophyll. The browning of many oak and beech leaves, however, is caused largely by oxidation processes such as take place in wounded and dying cells, which turn brown, just as a slice of apple does if it is left out in the air. The brilliant red and purple colors of red oak, red maple, sumac, Virginia creeper and sweet gum, however, are all due to anthocyanins. Since anthocyanins require high light intensities and high sugar content for their formation, they show up particularly on bright autumn days which have been preceded by a cold snap, which traps sugar in the leaves. This explains why the fall colors are exceptionally spectacular in certain years.

WE now have extracted a remarkable amount of information about the chemical composition of plants simply by tasting, smelling, looking and cooking. Since so many of the chemical processes in plants involve the absorption and release of gases which we can neither see nor smell, we must now go to the chemical or physiological laboratory to continue our research. And what we will examine there is, first of all, photosynthesis, the process by which plants transform light energy into chemical energy—the most important single chemical process in the world.

If that last statement sounds extravagant, let us pause for just a moment to consider what photosynthesis does. In terms of energy, there is nothing to compare with it: it makes green plants grow—all green plants, all over the world, from the wheat and corn of the Midwest to the cotton in Egypt, the lush flora of the rain forests of South America and the grass on the plains of Africa and Asia to the giant sequoias of California. And in terms of tonnage its production makes man's industries seem trifling. Every year the world's steel mills turn out 350 million tons of steel, the world's cement factories 325 million tons of cement. The world's green plants, however, produce 150 *billion* tons of sugar every year—and this by a process that no one has yet been able to reproduce in a test tube; a process, in fact, which we are only just beginning to understand.

The discovery of photosynthesis—or rather, the beginnings of its discovery—goes back some 200 years. At that time, it was known that if an animal was kept in a closed container it would gradually foul the air by breathing and would eventually suffocate. Why this was, no one knew, because the different gases which make up the air were not yet known. Not until Joseph Priestley discovered oxygen in 1774 did an explanation become possible: animals used up the life-giving oxygen and replaced it with suffocating carbon dioxide. Priestley then went on to find that plants seemed to reverse this process: they were able to ameliorate air which was fouled by animals or humans breathing it. This led to an unprecedented use of flowers in sickrooms, which in those days were generally kept tightly closed so that no "harmful" outside air could get in. But a Dutch physician and chemist of the times, Jan Ingen-Housz, was skeptical about this indiscriminate use of plants to help the ailing, and he carried out a number of experiments to prove or disprove its validity. The result was his discovery, in the course of a series of brilliant tests, that only the green parts of plants can ameliorate the air, and then only if they are placed in strong light. Flowers and other nongreen parts, he found, as well as green leaves left in darkness, used up oxygen just as animals did. Further experiments carried out by the Swiss Nicholas Théodore de Saussure helped finally to reduce the whole process to a chemical formula:

$$6CO_2 + 6H_2O + \text{light energy} \longrightarrow C_6H_{12}O_6 + 6O_2$$

carbon dioxide water   sugar oxygen

which is just the reverse of the formula shown on page 57, illustrating plant and animal respiration:

$$C_6H_{12}O_6 + 6O_2 \longrightarrow 6CO_2 + 6H_2O + \text{chemical energy.}$$

sugar oxygen carbon dioxide water

THESE two equations, illustrating the two major processes carried out by the plant, contain the secret of photosynthesis and the capture of energy from light. First, when green leaves are placed in strong light, they can use this light to make sugar and oxygen out of carbon dioxide and water. Second, they can then reverse the process, breaking down the sugar with oxygen—which is simple respiration—to release the energy absorbed from the light, with carbon dioxide and water as by-products. The transition from light energy via photosynthesis to chemical energy via sugar may be immediate or delayed, according to need: the energy is there, available in the chemically very stable sugar, and it can even be saved for millions of years, as in coal, finally to be used by man to heat his home or cook his food or drive his steam engines.

That is the outline of the story, but there is much more to it than that. How, for instance, is photosynthesis itself achieved? This is like asking how life begins—we just do not know the answer. But we do know two major principles.

The first is that the direct effect of light in photosynthesis is not on carbon dioxide, but on water—with the light somehow contributing to a breakdown of water molecules. It is in this process that chlorophyll plays its role. One result is the release of oxygen; the other is accumulation of chemical energy in the form of a very unstable compound called adenosine triphosphate, or ATP.

LIGHT MAKES SUGAR

Photosynthesis, in broad outline, is a four-part cycle. At the start, light reacts energetically with chlorophyll (1), splitting water into its basic components. This releases oxygen (exit arrow at top); far more importantly, it also charges two coenzymes, one with chemical energy and the other with hydrogen. The curved arrow (2) plots the action of these laden coenzymes. Waiting is carbon dioxide (entrance arrow at right above) in the grip of an "acceptor" compound (3). Here, one of the charged coenzymes discharges its load of energy to power the key union between the other's hydrogen load and the waiting carbon. The resulting carbohydrates become sugars (exit arrow, bottom), which form the basic products of photosynthesis. The two unladen coenzymes then return (4) to be recharged and continue the cycle.

The second principle is that the carbon dioxide in the air is reduced with this chemical energy in the form of ATP to form sugar. How do we know this? It was proved in dramatic fashion by the Nobel Prize-winning biochemist Melvin Calvin, who has made a series of ingenious experiments with radioactive carbon at the University of California. The usefulness of radioactive elements in such experiments is that the paths of individual molecules of the radioactive material can be traced through the chain of chemical reactions in the plant. Thus, when Calvin fed radioactive carbon dioxide in gaseous form to photosynthesizing green algae, he was able to follow the path of the "hot" carbon atoms after they entered the algae, just as one might follow the movement of a single blue marble being shaken up in a jar full of clear glass marbles. The path that Calvin's radioactive carbon molecules took was swift and direct. Within only a few seconds after their entry into the algae in gaseous form, they showed up inside individual cells—as parts of sugar molecules! With almost unbelievable speed the gas molecules had been grabbed by an as yet unknown ingredient in the plant cells where photosynthesis takes place, broken down and then, with the aid of ATP energy, built into molecules of sugar.

PIONEERS OF TWO CENTURIES

Joseph Priestley, 18th Century English amateur chemist, discovered that plants produced oxygen. He observed that air which suffocated mice in a sealed jar could keep other mice alive provided that plants were put in the jar, too. The 20th Century scientist Melvin Calvin used a radioactive tracer to discover how plants turn carbon dioxide into sugar. His studies won him the Nobel Prize in 1961.

Besides photosynthesis and respiration, there are a great many metabolic reactions occurring constantly and simultaneously in the humming chemical factory that is a plant cell. There is protoplasm to be synthesized, there are amino acids and purines and hundreds of other compounds to be made. All of them use the same energy source, sugar, but each must be produced in a specific amount and at the proper time. The regulators of all this activity are enzymes, special proteins which stimulate the various chemical reactions inside the cell. Each enzyme is partly or completely specific in the reactions it stimulates, and it is fair to say that there are as many different kinds of enzymes in a cell as there are kinds of substances made.

Yet in all of this diversity, there is a certain unity. For one thing, all enzymes are proteins, and it has been suggested that the same protein can do several jobs, changing its configuration to operate in different ways. For it is generally conceded that an enzyme, as a true catalyst, does not itself participate in the chemical reactions it stimulates—it only provides the proper conditions for the energy transfers involved by bringing the reactants together.

This principle, that a single chemical constituent or a few closely related ones can perform a large number of functions, is most perfectly exemplified by sugar. We have already seen how sugar is the first fully stable product of photosynthesis, produced by the billions of tons each year, more than any other chemical compound in the world. In addition to being the main product of photosynthesis, it is also one of the main *storage* products of chemical energy, and many plants such as sugar cane, sugar beets, onions, peas and sweet corn store it in stems, roots, bulbs or seeds. Yet for all of its chemical stability, sugar also is the main energy *source* for all plant and animal cells—that is to say, the moment it is needed, this chemically stable product can become so reactive that there is energy available for all cellular processes. The trigger that fires it is phosphate, provided by that same ATP that works so energetically in the photosynthesizing process. A sugar combined with phosphate abruptly becomes one of the most reactive compounds in the cell.

But if sugar molecules become very reactive when they combine with phosphates, they become equally nonreactive when the phosphates detach themselves again. Without phosphate, the long chains of sugar molecules that formed

in their phosphate phase may become cellulose, one of the most stable organic substances in existence. Cellulose in its various forms, like cotton, linen or paper, can even be treated with concentrated acids or alkali or other common solvents, and it still stays intact. As a matter of fact, once a plant has built cellulose into a cell wall it has begun to limit its ability to change the size or shape of that cell thereafter. Not only are most plants which produce cellulose powerless to break it down further, the same is true of animals. Cows, for example, live on grasses, but they do not digest the cellulose. It is chewed and mashed thoroughly until all the nourishment has been extracted from the cells, but the cells themselves—their cellulose walls—pass right through the animals and are eliminated in exactly the same chemical condition in which they entered. There is only one kind of animal known that can digest cellulose. That is the termite, and it needs a population of even smaller creatures, protozoa living in its intestine, to help it do the job. Cellulose is also resistant to most microorganisms, which explains why leaves and branches do not immediately decay when they fall to the forest floor. Only certain bacteria and fungi are capable of decomposing forest litter.

When the long chains of sugar molecules do not all come joined end to end, as in cellulose, but in a slightly different way, with occasional branches in the chain, a different kind of substance is formed. This is starch, a molecule too large to be soluble but one which nonetheless lacks the chemical resistance of cellulose. Starch is a sort of bulk-storage form of sugar, since it is readily broken down again inside the cell by an enzyme called diastase, and in that way may re-enter the chain of reactions. This may be demonstrated by the simple experiment of chewing some starch. Diastase is present in human saliva, and if the starch is chewed long enough it begins to taste sweet. Diastase is formed in all germinating seeds in which starch is a storage food. One of the best sources of diastase is malt, made from germinating barley seeds. By mixing a sufficient amount of malt with ground barley, its starch is transformed into sugar which then can be fermented by yeast to make beer.

THERE are a number of different kinds of sugars which are all closely related in a chemical sense, and it is only since the development of highly sophisticated laboratory techniques that we have been able readily to separate and distinguish them. Each of these sugars has different properties inside plant cells and produces slightly different products when it forms long molecular chains. Instead of cellulose, for example, hemicelluloses may be produced which can give the same strength to cell walls but which can be broken down again and reused by the plant for energy. Thus the cell walls themselves sometimes function as food storehouses, as in the pit of the date, whose cell walls, monstrously thick, can be dissolved when the seed germinates and needs food. With slight chemical modifications in the sugar molecules, the chains they form may also have completely different properties, as in many plant slimes and pectins. Plant slimes have a function in drought resistance: when a cactus is wounded, the slime inside the cell oozes out over the cut surface, then dries and seals off the cut very effectively. Pectins, as we have seen, provide a semirigidity to young plant cell walls before they are stiffened by cellulose.

All of these compounds come from a few relatively simple materials. The same basic chemical structure is used over and over to provide energy storage, energy supply, mechanical strength, tissue stiffness, mechanics for cell-wall growth and drought protection. This certainly is ingenuity of the highest order.

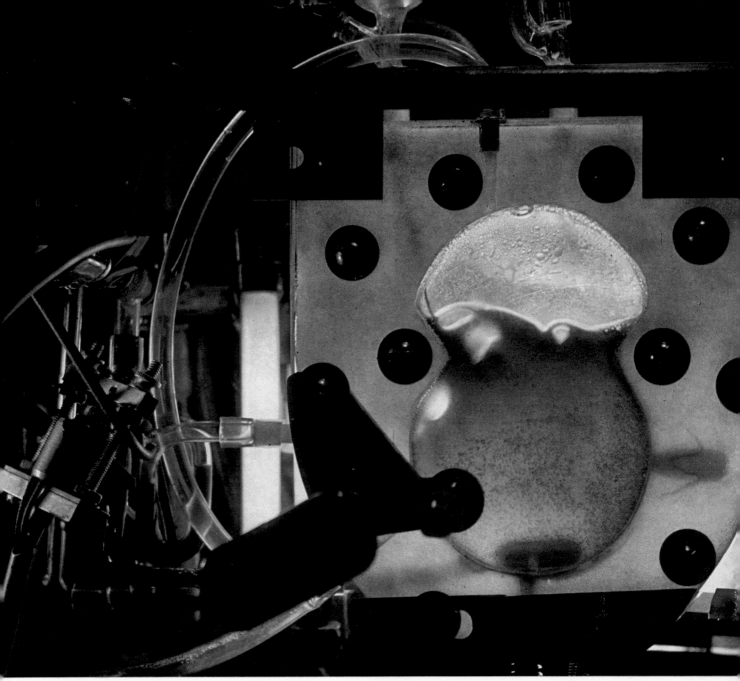

RADIOACTIVE CARBON DIOXIDE BUBBLES THROUGH GREEN ALGAE IN AN EXPERIMENT TO TRACE THE PATH OF CARBON IN PHOTOSYNTHESIS

The Wonders of Color

All green plants—even the minute algae above—are fantastically productive chemical works powered by sunlight, the fundamental source of all the energy, save atomic, on the earth. In the conversion of this energy to food by photosynthesis, one pigment—chlorophyll —plays the vital role; but many others contribute not only to the chemistry of plants but, spectacularly, to their appearance as well.

PHOTOSYNTHETIC
PRODUCTS (to storage)

WATER
VAPOR (out)

OXYGEN (out)

CARBON
DIOXIDE (in)

WATER (up)

STARCH
STORAGE

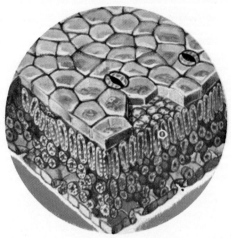

1 Rice-shaped vertical palisade cells and spongy cells below them are dotted with green chloroplasts, the tiny photosynthesis factories of the plant. This is an enlargement of the small, circled leaf area at left.

A Microcosm to Make

The wonders of photosynthesis have intrigued scientists ever since the phenomenon was first recognized. The over-all process—the conversion of water and carbon dioxide into sugar—has been known for at least a century. After all that time and despite endless man-hours of research, there still remain gaps in our understanding of photosynthesis. But our information is growing.

The plant at the left is a common sweet potato, with arrows indicating the routes of the basic raw materials and products in photosynthesis. The drawings on these pages depict increasing magnifications of the plant's photosynthesis mechanisms.

The heart of the process lies in the chloroplasts, with their light-reacting pigment, which are shown above in the cells of a leaf. Chlorophyll absorbs light heavily in the red and blue range of the sunlight spectrum as it strikes the leaf (*left above*) and gains most of its energy from these wavelengths. Water, of course, is already present, having been drawn up through the roots. And there is also carbon dioxide, which entered the leaf through its many pores. The light-activated chlorophyll first splits the water molecule, yielding a hydrogen atom and releasing some oxygen into the air. The hydrogen is instantly seized in the grip of a special escort molecule; in the next step it will play a crucial role.

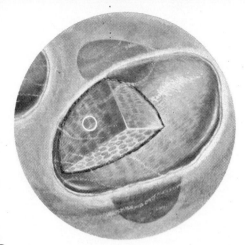

2 Football-shaped chloroplasts, shown in a higher magnification of the circled area at left, have a monopoly on all chlorophyll in the cell. They can turn within the cell to take best advantage of the light.

3 Coin-shaped grana in chloroplasts are revealed by a still higher magnification. Stacked one upon another, they show the thin layers of chlorophyll, where the reaction with the light waves takes place.

Food from Sunlight

In this process, however, some split molecules of water reunite. In so doing, they release energy, which is used to create, from material already present in the plant, the energy-laden driver molecule called ATP, or adenosine triphosphate. ATP, a universal power unit in living organisms, has the ability to supply energy to chemical reactions without itself becoming part of the end product. This ends the "photo," or light-requiring, phase of photosynthesis; at this point, the work of chlorophyll is finished and the remaining reactions are entirely chemical.

The carbon dioxide, meanwhile, lines up with an "acceptor" molecule that is stored in the plant. It is now that the stage is set for the critical union. The hydrogen atom, gripped in its escort molecule and powered by ATP, combines with the lined-up pair to form a highly reactive compound, designated PGA (for phosphoglyceric acid). The PGA molecules then combine to form sugar.

The machinery for these virtually instantaneous reactions is extremely complex, but with the electron microscope much of it can actually be seen. The final stage in these magnifications at the right is on the molecular level—yet even here, biophysicists have been able to reconstruct, with plausible exactitude, the nature and position of these minute instruments in the most productive chemical factory on earth.

4 Bead-shaped quantasomes, revealed under the cover of a granum in a further magnification, are the individual photosynthetic units. Each tiny bead contains some 200 light-sensitive chlorophyll molecules.

5 Jagged chlorophyll molecules, tilted as in this stylized drawing, are interspersed with orange carotene molecules which can absorb certain light waves and thus transfer extra solar energy to the chlorophyll.

SELDOM FOUND IN THE BLOSSOMS OF FLOWERING PLANTS, CHLOROPHYLL STRIPES THE PETALS OF THIS HYBRID TRILLIUM WITH BOLD GREEN

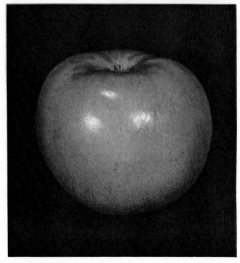

CHLOROPHYLL COLORS A RHODE ISLAND GREENING

Green—the Basic Pigment

Quite apart from the wonders of its chemical powers, chlorophyll is basically a pigment and lends its green color to the majority of plants. But it is obviously only one of the thousands of pigments found in botanical life, particularly in flowers and fruits. More than a hundred years of research have left largely unexplained the function of these pigments as coloring agents—if there is any. It can, however, be assumed that they probably help to attract insects and other animals, first for the purpose of pollination and later to assist in seed distribution. For this reason, perhaps, chlorophyll by itself is the only coloring agent found in many wind-pollinated flowers—the wind would have no eyes for the beauty, say, of a golden daffodil *(right above)*.

A BRILLIANT YELLOW DAFFODIL DERIVES ITS COLOR FROM ONE OF MANY CAROTENOID PIGMENTS. CAROTENOIDS ALSO MAKE TOMATOES RED

Carotenoids—Bright and Durable

Carotenoid pigments, which also absorb light for photosynthesis, are frequently found in chromoplasts, structures in the cell which brightly color fruits and flowers like those shown on this page. More than 60 varieties of carotenoid compounds have been isolated. They make up the plant world's second family of color. Divided into two major groups, the carotenes and xanthophylls, they range from lemon yellow to tomato red. Carotenoids are thought by some botanists to play an important role in the light-influenced, or phototropic, movements of plants, and animals derive vitamin A from them. So durable are the carotenoids that these pigments survive the digestive processes of animals and wind up as the coloring matter in egg yolks and butterfat.

CAROTENES PREDOMINATE IN A GOLDEN DELICIOUS

67

A RED ARUM, REPLETE WITH ANTHOCYANIN PIGMENTS, DISPLAYS A LEAF OF FIERY CRIMSON. ITS YELLOW SPADIX BEARS INDIVIDUAL FLOWERS

ANTHOCYANINS MAKE A JONATHAN RED

Anthocyanins—the Reds and Blues

The plant world's third family of color is produced by the anthocyanin pigments, which range in shades from palest pink through red to flamboyant purple. Their brilliant hues are contained in solution in the plant's cell sap. Despite lengthy research, no vital function has ever been unequivocally assigned to these decorative pigments. It is known that the anthocyanins are readily influenced by such factors as relative acidity. One species of morning-glory, for example, begins its daily cycle in the morning with slightly acid cell sap and a pale pink color, and winds up in the evening mildly alkaline and blue in color. The hydrangea offers a classic example: in neutral soil, its flowers will be red, but they turn blue under alkaline conditions.

AN AFRICAN VIOLET gets its color from an anthocyanin pigment called violanin, a close chemical relative to the pigment which colors delphiniums. The genetic behavior of anthocyanins is so well understood that African violet growers, by selection, can produce specimens throughout the whole spectrum of anthocyanin coloring, from pink to blue—and white as well.

THE TRANQUIL AUTUMN BEAUTY along this rural New Hampshire road stems from a chemical reaction, repeated a millionfold in turning leaves, in which pigments and weather play an equal role. As the season of leaf growth ends, the production of chlorophyll, whose green pigment has predominated throughout the spring and summer, wanes and the yellow carotenoids

at last reveal themselves, particularly in elms, birches and poplars. In oaks and maples, anthocyanins form in the presence of sugar trapped in the leaves by sudden cold snaps and flaunt their brilliant reds. This yearly display is usually most spectacular in New England, where early frosts followed by warm spells commonly occur and deciduous trees are abundant.

4

Moving Water by Molecules and by Tons

As we look over the green carpet with which most of our earth is covered—
its tall trees, its dense shrubbery, its meadowlands, all occasionally spotted with bright flowers—we are struck immediately by the intimate relationship of plants to water. Where there is no water there are no plants; the true
desert areas of earth are barren. And so it is clear that while water is only one of
the many substances on which plants depend, it is one of the most basic and
important ones. Just as it was the medium in which life first began, so it is essential if life is to burgeon and grow. All chemical reactions that take place
within the cell occur in a watery medium; it is by means of water that all substances are transported to all other parts of the organism. In short, nothing goes
on in a plant when there is no water.

The clearest proof for this last statement is the seed. A seed may be completely dry, its life suspended, with no chemical reactions occurring, no sign of
any vitality at all—yet with water it will revive. In its inert condition it can
withstand extremes of temperature, far below freezing or near the boiling point
of water (though not *in* water, of course); it can be kept for long periods of time,
for hundreds, perhaps thousands of years; then, when it is given water, it begins

73

to respire—which is to say it starts active life. Molecules of water penetrate its outer coat, and various vital processes commence inside it. This begins when the water content of a seed reaches eight per cent of its total bulk; below that, it is inert. Above 12 per cent, it has enough water to germinate and commence growing. In between, there is only enough water to start the processes of respiration. The seed will "stir," as it were, but it will not come to proper life. If it gets no further water, it will slowly burn up its food reserves, finally losing its power to germinate, and eventually will die. That explains why seeds on the shelves of stores will keep for only a couple of years; there is enough moisture in ordinary air for very slow respiration, but not enough to support growth. In a very dry climate they will keep longer; but even in the desert tombs of the Egyptian Pharaohs there is some moisture and, contrary to popular belief, the 4,000-year-old seeds that have been found there will not germinate.

The oldest authenticated viable seeds, those of a lotus from Japan, revived and grew when they were dug out of the acid substratum of a bog and given fresh, pure water. Experiments to test the viability of seeds kept in a vacuum are being conducted right now, but it will be another thousand years before our descendants know what the final results of those experiments will be. So far, after 10 years' storage, there has been absolutely no change of viability in 50 different kinds of seeds. But even in a vacuum some species have a tendency to lose their viability.

THE plain fact is that although so many plants and animals long ago became landlubbers, they never really emancipated themselves from water. They need it to begin life and they need it incessantly until they die. Perhaps the simplest solution of the water problem was that hit on by the land animals: they brought their water with them in the form of blood and developed relatively waterproof skins to keep it stored within their bodies. But to replenish water lost by breathing, perspiration and bodily excretion, animals still must drink—which means that they must have access to water in liquid form, which, in turn, means water collected in large enough amounts so that it will flow or can be lapped up. This limits them in the choice of their environment—for instance, no large land animals can live in arid lands where surface water is lacking.

Plants, however, have almost no such limitation because they have developed an entirely different way of satisfying their water needs. In the first place, they can gather water in minute quantities from the soil. They are much more efficient accumulators than animals, and once they get themselves established in even the driest places they can prosper—provided their roots reach down deep to invisible sources of water—as long as the source remains. But if the water source disappears, then even a desert plant will, in time, disappear too. Unlike an animal, it cannot pick itself up and move to another place where there may be water.

A plant could not have a waterproof skin in the sense that animals do, so it has different problems. It needs to draw carbon dioxide in through its leaves for photosynthesis, and since one gas will go out where another goes in, it loses water vapor from its leaves—a fact which has an important bearing on its water supply system, as we shall see. A typical plant may lose up to a hundred times as much water per unit of weight than a mammal in a given period. Thus, if a plant had to fill the water needs of its cells as mammals do, by the circulation of some form of blood, the blood would have to circulate and be replenished at an impossibly fast rate.

How, then, do plants solve their water problems? They do it with an intricate plumbing system which has its beginning in the roots, where water is absorbed from the soil, continues through a complex of tubes which carry water to all parts of the plant, and ends with the water being diffused from the leaves into the surrounding air. This sounds simple enough, but it poses some difficult questions, the first being: how do the roots actually get the water?

This is accomplished by a process known as osmosis, the absorption of a liquid through a cell's surface. Young plant roots are covered with innumerable tiny root hairs. These penetrate the most minute crannies in the soil, and wherever they encounter a bit of moisture their cells take it in. Dead cells will not do this, as can be demonstrated by a simple experiment. A willow branch stuck in the ground will soon strike root and absorb all the water it needs. But a dead stick planted next to it will absorb hardly any water at all. The mechanics of this phenomenon were worked out some 150 years ago by a French physician, René Joachim Henri Dutrochet. He took a pig's bladder, an organic, so-called semipermeable membrane which was the nearest thing to a cell membrane that he could find, and put it over the wide end of a funnel filled with a salt solution. He then placed the funnel, with its membrane end down, in a pan of water. Almost immediately the salt solution in the funnel started to expand, apparently taking up water from the pan through the membrane. The obvious explanation was that the cell walls actually were selective—able to let water molecules in, but at the same time able to prevent salt and sugar molecules from going out. The salt solution, furthermore, was able to attract water. The more concentrated the salt solution, the more water was sucked up, to the point where considerable pressures were built up in the funnel. A six per cent salt solution (one teaspoon of salt in a teacup of water) produced a pressure of 50 atmospheres. Since one atmosphere equals 15 pounds of pressure per square inch, this is a remarkable figure; it is the equal of the high pressures that may be found inside steam engines.

Dutrochet's instrument, called an osmometer, has its counterpart in every living cell, including those of plants. In an earlier chapter we have already seen how the living protoplasm of plant cells keeps such dissolved substances as anthocyanins, tannins and sugars held inside the vacuole. It is those substances, dissolved in the water of the vacuole, which, through the process of osmosis, attract water into the cell through its semipermeable membrane, replacing the water it has lost. As more water is absorbed, pressure builds up inside the cell. When this osmotic pressure equals the counterpressure of the rather inflexible cell wall—like the bladder of a football being blown up inside its leather casing—no more water can be brought in. The cell wall simply will not stretch beyond a certain limit.

THE inner pressure that cells can generate explains another characteristic of plants, their so-called turgor. Like an inflated football, the wall of a cell under osmotic pressure becomes taut. This tautness, multiplied many thousands of times in all of the individual cells of a plant's stem, branches and leaves, gives them enormous stiffness. When the plant loses water in the form of vapor to the open air, the turgor of the cells decreases and the stiffness of the plant decreases too. When, through lack of water, the turgor has disappeared completely, the leaves and the herbaceous stems become increasingly limp and the plant wilts.

It is possible to destroy the turgor in another way—by destroying the semi-

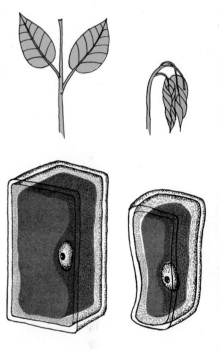

FROM TURGOR TO WILT

When water is plentiful, all cells fill to capacity, achieving the fluid-rich state called turgor. The soft stem parts stand erect, the leaves are stiff. In such a turgid plant, each plant cell's central vacuole is charged with water (left) and the surrounding protoplasm is pushed out to the limits of the cell wall, stretching it tight. When the plant loses more water through transpiration than it can absorb through its roots, the cell walls partially deflate after the vacuole shrinks. The plant's turgor decreases and it begins to wilt. If no water is brought up from the roots, the cell walls turn limp (right). The plant now wilts completely and dies.

permeability of the cell membranes, thus releasing the sugars and salts within them. Extreme heat will do this: if we dip spinach or lettuce leaves in boiling water, they become limp as if they were wilted. There are, however, plants and parts of plant stems which do not become limp through cooking; these, as we have seen in Chapter 2, derive their stiffness from rigid cell walls, like those in wood and fibers, and boiling does not affect their strength.

Water movement by osmosis is slow—as slow as the mixing of sugar in the bottom of a teacup when the tea is not stirred with a spoon—and there is, demonstrably, a definite limit to the amount a single cell can take up. However, cells can pass water from one to another if there is a difference in absorptive power between them. If one cell loses some water, its cell-wall pressure will decrease, but its osmotic potential will not, since its salts and sugars are retained. This cell can then "drink" from a neighboring cell whose water supply may be greater. The neighbor, in turn, can absorb water from a still less thirsty neighbor, and so on. Thus we may have a chain of cells, one end of which is in contact with a supply of water in the soil while the other end is losing it to the air. The cells in between will show differences in water-absorbing capacity and thus will be able to pass water along from one to another by osmosis. The cell nearest to the water (a root-hair cell, for example) will have the smallest absorptive capacity; the one at the other end of the chain will be the thirstiest, with the largest absorptive power. To keep the water moving along the chain a fairly high difference in absorptive capacity between neighboring cells is needed, about one half atmosphere under normal conditions. Since the osmotic pull of ordinary plant cells ranges between 10 and 20 atmospheres, it follows that there must be a limit to the number of cells in such an osmotic chain and thus to the size of plants. We know that the average cell is about four thousandths of an inch in diameter; therefore any plant that moved water entirely by osmosis would have to be less than a quarter of an inch tall. And this is exactly what the earliest primitive land plants were: thin leaflike affairs (liverworts and fern prothallia are probably their closest modern counterparts), lying flat on the moist soil, sometimes penetrating into it with hairlike structures, called rhizoids, on their lower sides.

Most modern land plants, however, are a great deal taller than a quarter of an inch. How do they move their water around?

Osmotic water movement clearly is not enough to do it, although it does play an important part in the plant's water movement. It is the vital beginning, since it gets the water to the pipes that service the plant. Inside the roots another phenomenon we do not yet entirely understand forces the water into the water vessels which carry it upward. This produces a positive pressure which in turn causes guttation, the formation of water droplets at the edge of plant leaves in the early morning, and also makes a tree stump "bleed" for days or weeks after it has been cut, with almost pure water running out of its cut surface, especially near the edges. This bleeding sap comes out with great force, and at one time it was believed that it was indeed root pressure that forced water to the tops of the tallest trees. This theory, however, had to be abandoned when experiments with pressure gauges inserted into the base of a tree trunk showed that a high level of root pressure occurred only just after sunrise. During the morning, the pressure decreased rapidly, until finally there was no pressure reading at all, but rather a negative pressure, or suction. Thus it was clear that root pressure could at best be only part of the answer: it ceases to function just at the time when a plant begins to need water most—the hot sunny hours in the middle of the day.

The true answer to water movement in plants lies in mass flow by streaming. This is the same principle on which our home plumbing operates: water enters the pipes of a house under pressure, is distributed to all of the various faucets, toilets, baths and lawn sprinklers, and from them passes into the air again. In the larger land plants we find just such a plumbing system, fully developed, in the long, tubular cells or vessels carrying the water from the water-absorbing cells in the roots to the topmost and outermost extremities. To understand the major force involved in pumping water through all the tubes and veins of a plant, we must consider a phenomenon that takes place at the outlets of the system, the leaf surfaces. This, too, is a diffusion process like osmosis, but one that involves the movement of water molecules through the walls of leaf cells outward into the open air. This loss of water through the leaves and into the atmosphere is called transpiration.

Wᴵᵀᴴ water coming into the root hairs of a plant by osmosis and evaporating out of the leaves by transpiration, it is clear that there must be a fairly steady flow of water through the plant. It is also clear that if the plant is to keep from wilting, its water loss at one end must be balanced by what it is able to pick up from the soil at the other. This suggests that the rates of input and output must be about equal. This they are, if expressed as total amount. However, there is an important difference between the water-absorbing potential of root hairs and the several-hundredfold higher water-absorbing potential of air at the other end of the system where the leaves are. This difference is balanced by the several-hundredfold greater absorptive surface of the root hairs. Because of this they are able to supply all the water which the leaves lose by transpiration —but it is the high absorptive potential of dry air which furnishes the power by which water can be sucked up from the roots for distances of hundreds of feet by the largest trees.

Given this tremendous potential of dry air, it is obvious that there must be some way of controlling it, otherwise a plant might dry out completely if for any reason the supply of ground water is reduced or even temporarily cut off by a dry spell in the weather. There *is* a control system and it is a most ingenious one, built into the leaf at the point where transpiration occurs and serving the dual function of regulating not only the loss of water but also the intake of air with its essential carbon dioxide. To see just how this works, let us focus our microscope on a leaf section and examine the transport systems through which it is supplied with water and air.

There are, actually, two such transport systems—one hooked up to the plumbing system that brings up water from the roots, and another that leads to the outside of the leaf, to the open air. Both are essential to the main function of the leaf, the transformation of light energy into chemical energy through photosynthesis. And since a leaf has to be a thin structure, with its cells spread widely in layers so as to absorb as much light as possible, its internal plumbing has to operate efficiently within a very restricted space—and it does. In fact, no single cell in the entire structure of the leaf is more than 10 to 20 cells removed from some part of the system which supplies it with the water that it needs.

Water comes to the leaf cells through thin bundles of tubelike cells radiating outward from the larger vascular bundles in the midrib. These bundles divide into smaller and smaller veinlets which reach into the farthest corners of the leaf, and from them the cells draw water as needed. But while these veinlets are connected with the plumbing system in the inside of the plant, access to the air outside is provided by a system of air channels which lead to a multitude of tiny pores in the leaf's tough, transparent outer skin, or epidermis, composed of many cells. If the water supply of the cells is adequate, they can afford to lose part of it through these air channels; at the same time they have access through these open channels to the carbon dioxide from the atmosphere.

The pores themselves contain the mechanism which controls the rate of water loss. They have been given the aptly descriptive Greek name of stomata, meaning "little mouths." A plant's water-control system depends on the stomata, which can be opened or closed by the action of two cells bordering each stoma. The opening mechanism functions according to the water supply in the leaf: when there is plenty of water, the cells along the sides of the stomata are swelled up, and since the cells are thicker at their ends, like miniature crescent-shaped beans, the swelling has the effect of separating the thinner middle sections to form an open slit. When the cell turgor decreases—i.e., when the leaf needs water—the shrinking of the cells along the sides of each stoma causes the slit to narrow and even to close, so that transpiration is greatly decreased until the cells have replenished themselves and the stomata open up again.

This system works automatically and very efficiently most of the time. It is only under conditions of prolonged drought that a plant will wilt permanently, since even with closed stomata the leaf surface is not 100 per cent watertight, and under the tremendous pull of dry air will continue to leak small but critical amounts of water until the plant is dead. However, there is another built-in factor that helps serve as an equalizer. Given a sufficient amount of time, a plant can expand its root system to search out more water and thus restore the balance. A four-month-old winter rye plant, for example, was found to have roots totaling 387 miles in length, which means that it grew roots at the rate of more than three miles per day—and developed root hairs at the rate of more than 100 million daily. This produced a total water absorptive surface of more than 6,875 square feet—a striking illustration of what plants can achieve in terms of taking water from the soil.

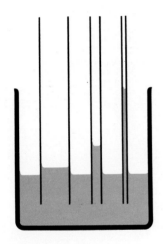

AN UPWARD CRAWL

Water molecules have two physical attributes (seen above and opposite) that are important in the circulation system of a plant. The first is adhesion, the force that attracts water molecules to the walls of a container. As this drawing shows, the tendency to adhere makes the water crawl upward in a tube. The narrower the tube, the higher the water will rise. Even in the wide vessel containing the three tubes, adhesion has the effect of causing the water to curve upward slightly at each edge. Adhesion is the basis of capillary action, which helps the water in a plant's narrow sap vessels to rise.

THE crucial part of all this is still the fact that the leaves, through the open stomata, can make use of the difference in moisture gradient between the roots and the leaves to pull up water all through the plant's system. At this point the physicists among my students will lift a warning finger: how is it possible for water to be pulled up through a large plant, like a tree, for such distances? We know that there is a limit to the amount of pull a pump can exert on water before the column of water being pumped up collapses. That limit is 15 pounds per square inch, and the highest a pump can pull is 30 feet. How, then, can a sequoia tree pump water 10 times as high?

This is the problem the 19th Century botanists were up against. Perhaps, they reasoned, the living cells in the wood acted as pumps—but this possibility was ruled out by some spectacular experiments in which every wood cell was killed over a vertical stem or trunk length of 40 feet. The German botanist Eduard Strasburger did this by boiling a 40-foot coiled stem section of a wisteria vine in a cauldron, after which he strung it back onto his rooftop 40 feet from the ground. The leaves on the vine did not wilt, showing that they could still pull up water beyond what was thought to be physically possible without the aid of living cells. In other experiments he was able to show that in trees over 40 feet high the water moved up regularly with no sign of wilting, even when all the wood cells had been killed with a powerful poison.

Some as yet unknown physical principle clearly was involved in the upward movement of water in plant stems. And five years after Strasburger's experiments, in 1891 it was at last discovered: the principle of "cohesion." Simply described, cohesion is the phenomenon by which water molecules cling tightly together and resist being pulled apart—the same phenomenon which makes it possible, by careful handling, to fill a cup full of water to slightly above the brim. In a thin tube, cohesion can be quite a considerable force—in a plant cell it actually takes many thousands of pounds per square inch before the threadlike, confined water column can be pulled apart and a vacuum is created. Therefore the leaf *can* effectively exert a pull of a hundred atmospheres, or thousands of pounds per square inch, on the water in a plant's plumbing system—and therefore water *can* be pulled up to the tops of trees hundreds of feet tall, such as the tallest redwoods in California, of which the highest reaches 364 feet into the sky, or the 300-foot eucalyptus trees of Australia.

Most of the water in the soil is rain water and theoretically it should be as pure as distilled water. Fortunately, however, this is usually not the case, for plants need not only water to live, but also minerals—vital salts which are liberated during the decomposition of rock and soil. This decomposition is a continuous process and proceeds fastest at high temperatures. When there is plenty of rain, most of the salts produced by decomposition are washed away into streams and rivers, and a proper mineral balance is maintained. In desert areas, however, more salts may be produced than can be washed away by the scanty rainfalls, and salt accumulations may become so high that the soil has more salts than the plant cells. Under such conditions, the process of osmosis would be reversed: water would be extracted *from* the plants growing in such saline soils and they would become dehydrated and die. Actually, no plants will even germinate in such salty soil, and thus we find "alkaline flats" in desert areas where not a single plant will grow, as in the Great Salt Lake Desert or around the Dead Sea in Palestine.

The salt concentration in the ocean is also high, and very few land plants (except mangrove trees, which have certain special adaptations) grow in sea water. Most plants which grow on beaches, such as the coconut palm, actually live on fresh water, paradoxical though this may seem. The seashore may be their habitat because the ocean currents will distribute their seeds, the coconuts, but they can no more live on salt water than any other plant. In fact, their roots do not reach sea water, but only go down to the fresh water which, being lighter than the salt, floats on top of it. Thus, when it rains on the sandy tropical beaches, the rain water raises the water table in the sand, forcing the salt water downward and outward. This is the same phenomenon that makes it possible to pump fresh water from a short piece of pipe driven into the ground in seashore areas, where deep wells produce only salt water. This principle also explains why the salty soils of the Zuider Zee in Holland could be used for the growing of sugar beets and barley only a few years after they were reclaimed. During the first few years after the sea water had been drained, the rains produced two and a half feet of fresh water per year, which pushed down the sea water, and soon a thick enough layer of fresh water was formed to allow sugar beets and barley to grow and mature. If these crops had needed more than the two and a half feet of fresh water, they would have caused a rise in the

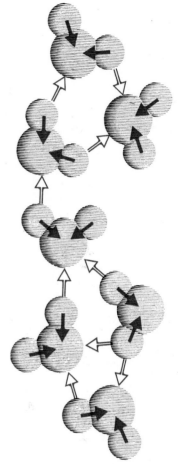

AN UPWARD HAUL

The power of cohesion (see diagram above) is the second attribute of water important in plant circulation. In every water molecule, the pair of hydrogen atoms (small spheres) is linked (colored arrows) to a single oxygen atom (larger sphere). At the same time, the hydrogen atoms are attracted to the oxygen atom of the nearest water molecule (white arrows). This secondary attraction can produce a tensile strength of as much as 2,000 pounds or more per square inch in a thin column of purified water. Cohesion thus helps a plant raise water many times higher than any pump can hoist it.

salt-water table and the land would have had to be abandoned for cultivation.

The lengths to which plants may and do go in their search for water, and their adaptability to varying conditions of water supply, is well illustrated by desert and steppe plants. These live under conditions of apparent water shortage—yet a good number of them thrive. Actually, many of them which we consider drought resistant are in reality drought escaping—i.e., they try to overcome the prevailing drought conditions in various ways rather than developing resistance to them. The seeds of all desert annuals, for instance, are quiescent until enough rain has fallen so that the desert soil holds enough water for them to grow, flower and ripen their seed. This accounts for the fact that the desert blooms only on the rare occasions when there has been heavy rain at the right time—usually October or November—to make these plants germinate.

But there are also the desert plants called phreatophytes, which reach down with their roots to underground reservoirs. These do such a remarkable job of seeking out permanent water supplies that man has learned to follow them and dig wells where they grow. The mesquite is such a water indicator—it will grow only where there is permanent water within 30 feet of the surface—and many wells in the California desert have been dug between mesquite shrubs. The cottonwood tree similarly is likely to indicate the presence of an underground stream with abundant water for irrigation only 10 feet down. The California fan palm, too, will grow only where water is close to the surface.

Succulents with swollen stems or thickened leaves, on the other hand, do not rely on any permanent water supply—they store up water in their tissues, like the ice plant with its thick, fleshy leaves or the familiar desert cacti with their barrel-like trunks and swollen branches. These plants all have a very thick cuticle covering stems and leaves and they lose little water by transpiration. In the infrequent desert rains, they can gorge themselves to the limit and thus survive through the long dry periods. There are some barrel cacti which can live for more than a year on just one full load of water.

STILL other desert plants have adapted to drought conditions by making their root system so efficient that the last vestiges of water in the most minute quantities can be reached and exploited. The creosote bush is one of these, with roots that penetrate far and wide. After a long rainless period, however, these plants, like any others, will begin to suffer from drought. But the American pygmy cedar (*Peucephyllum*) can forego soil water entirely: amazingly enough, it is able to live on the water vapor of the air alone, replenishing its supply each night, when even on the desert the air may become near saturated. One plant of the Sahara, the caper plant (*Capparis spinosa*), seems to have that same ability—like the pygmy cedar, it remains lush and green under the most severe soil drought conditions. Both plants may live under these extreme desert conditions precariously attached to exposed rock, certainly the poorest source of water for their roots.

Thus, among the 250,000 species of flowering plants, we know of just two which have really emancipated themselves from water in its liquid form—all others need it continuously or intermittently. They need it not only to carry out the vital process of photosynthesis, which is their main source of energy, but also to keep themselves supplied with the nutrients derived from the soil, necessary for continued growth. What these nutrients are, how plants utilize them and how man has learned to augment them artificially to grow bigger and better crops will be dealt with in a later chapter.

NOT MORNING DEW, BUT EXCESS WATER OOZING FROM THE PLANT ITSELF FORMS THESE DROPLETS ON THE EDGES OF STRAWBERRY LEAVES

A Lifelong Need

A plant's need for water starts when it is a seed, and its demands increase throughout its lifetime. Taken in by the roots, water is used in all chemical reactions, carries nutrients, keeps the plant rigid and at last passes out of the leaves as vapor or liquid. To ensure their water supply, plants have evolved extremely efficient plumbing systems and even ways of storing water against drought.

A DEMONSTRATION OF OSMOSIS fixes a semipermeable membrane over a glass funnel containing a sugar solution and immerses it in water. Water diffuses upward, diluting the solution until an equilibrium is achieved between the two fluids. Meanwhile, increasing pressure raises the solution in the tube.

How Water Rises in a Plant

The upward movement of water in plants begins in the fine root hairs made up of single cells. By the process of osmosis *(left)*, ground water diffuses into these cells through their semipermeable walls, diluting the dissolved sugars, salts and other sap substances held there. As more and more water dilutes the cell sap, osmotic pressure increases until the cell walls are stretched to their physical limit and the cells become turgid. Osmosis occurs through root hairs and the cells of the roots themselves as water passes to the main vessel leading to the stem. The accumulated turgor in these cells produces the phenomenon of root pressure, which is sufficient to move water into the plant's stem or trunk and is the impetus for guttation, the early-morning release of liquid water at the edges of plant leaves. However, the force that raises tons of water to the summit of a giant sequoia or ounces of water up a violet is a quite different one, resulting from transpiration, the plant's loss of water vapor through millions of pores on the surfaces of its leaves. A single corn plant may transpire more than two quarts of water a day, and an acre of corn more than 300,000 gallons in a season. This water can only be replenished by the roots, and it streams in myriads of thin tubes through the stem and all the branches of the plant, pulled upward by the suction in the leaves, its thousands of rising columns held together by the cohesive nature of water itself. Below and at right, the entire plumbing system of a typical hardwood tree, from root-hair cells to the cells that control transpiration in the leaves, is shown longitudinally and in cross section.

MICROSCOPIC ROOT HAIRS, seen at right in an enlarged detail of the section boxed on the facing page, search out moisture in the soil and increase the absorbing surface of the roots by as much as 20 times. These myriad threads may be injured in transplanting unless guarded by a ball of earth. As shown here, water and dissolved nutrients enter the root hairs by osmosis and are diffused through layers of root cells to the main vessel system going up the tree trunk to the leaves.

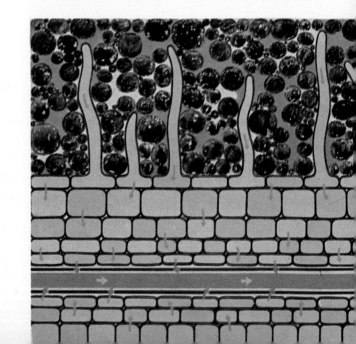

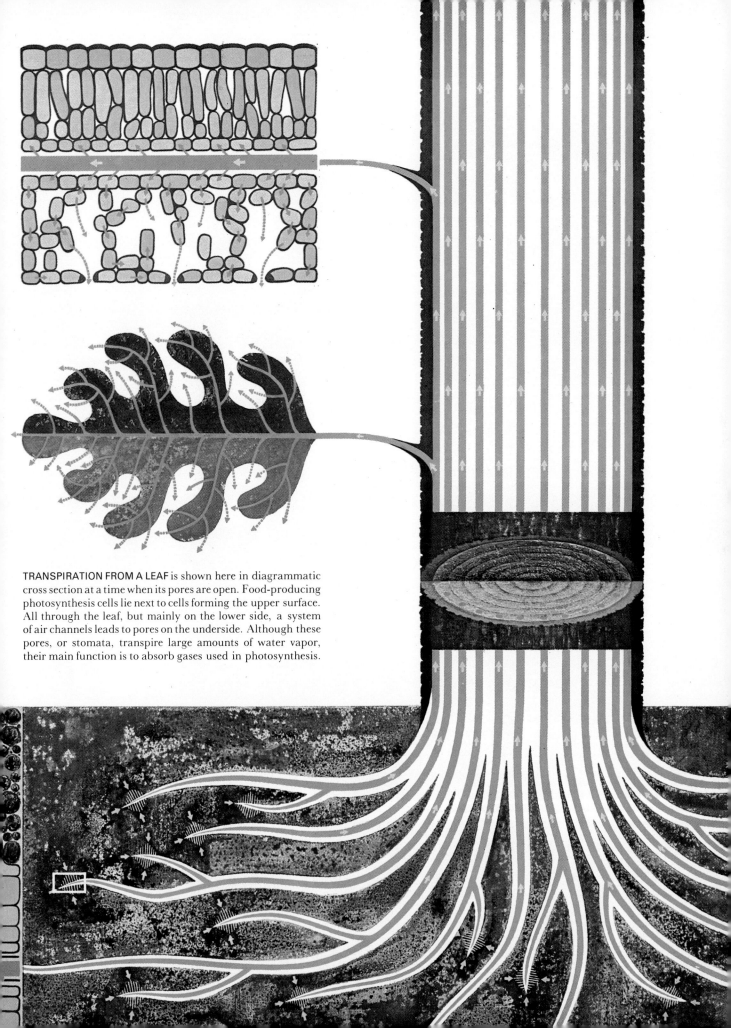

TRANSPIRATION FROM A LEAF is shown here in diagrammatic cross section at a time when its pores are open. Food-producing photosynthesis cells lie next to cells forming the upper surface. All through the leaf, but mainly on the lower side, a system of air channels leads to pores on the underside. Although these pores, or stomata, transpire large amounts of water vapor, their main function is to absorb gases used in photosynthesis.

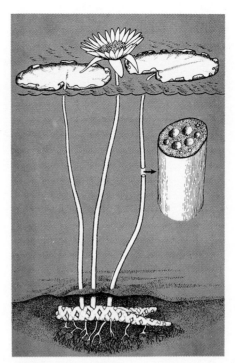

PERISCOPELIKE STEMS of a water lily have several large channels to get air to the roots.

A Problem of Surfeit

The water dwellers of the plant kingdom are known as hydrophytes. Some, like members of the duckweed family, float on ponds. Others are submerged—sedges and water plants that form underwater meadows but raise tiny white flowers above the water; pickerel weed and water lilies which, rooted in the bottom, send long stems up to the air. Since these plants live in a surfeit of water, their problem is to find and conserve air supplies, and they have become highly specialized for this purpose. Submerged plants can utilize the sunlight penetrating to depths of 15 or 20 feet for photosynthesis and absorb dissolved gases through a permeable outer covering. Those that float or are emergent, with direct access to the air, pipe it down from the leaves to the stem and even into the roots through numerous intercellular channels.

TROPICAL WATER LILIES rise high out of the water, getting the best of two worlds. Lily pads function like the leaves of land plants, but have pores on the upper surface only and no water-repellent coating.

85

WELL-WATERED, a thick-leaved succulent, *Bryophyllum (left)*, a plant of arid habitat, stands with a Temperate Zone *Coleus* during an experiment to demonstrate relative wilt resistance.

WITHOUT WATER, both plants are dead. But the *Bryophyllum*, storing more water and transpiring less, lived over 120 hours, while the *Coleus* wilted permanently in 36 hours.

PEGLIKE LEAVES characterize this drought-resistant succulent, Madagascar's *Kalanchoë tubiflora*. Bearing few stomata, each leathery leaf has enlarged cells that store reserve water.

A Problem of Drought

What causes plant leaves to droop or roll up on a hot summer afternoon, only to appear stiff and fresh again the next morning? The answer lies in the osmotic pressure or turgor in the leaf cells. This pressure generally declines during the daylight hours, when the plant is chemically most active, and rises overnight as the plant's root system replenishes the water supply. Under different weather conditions, however, the normal daily cycle varies. On a cool cloudy day, for example, leaf turgor may not drop at all and the pores, or stomata, controlling transpiration on the leaf surface, will remain open. But on an extremely hot, dry day, the stomata may close early in the morning as a guard against excessive water loss.

Under drought conditions, plants wilt and cannot recover unless they receive a fresh supply of water before their cells die. Unable to draw moisture from the soil, all the root, stem and leaf cells undergo a sort of reverse osmosis. A negative pressure reaction travels down through the plant, shrinking and breaking up its cell structure. Species that have adapted to semiarid climates, however, are able to withstand considerable periods of drought. The thick-leaved plants known as succulents possess relatively few stomata and their leaf surfaces are often shiny with an abundance of water-retaining wax. The cacti, most familiar of desert plants, depend for resistance to drought on widespread root networks that drink to the utmost from chance rainfall. Such random accumulations of water are then transferred to the plant's fleshy parts for storage.

86

STOMATA OF A TURK'S-CAP LILY, shown here in a micropho-
tograph of the leaf, form dozens of "little mouths" in various
stages of opening and closing. Each one is bordered by a pair of
guard cells so formed that an increase in water content forces
the stoma open. When turgor decreases, the guard cells shrink
and little or no moisture passes through the closed stoma.

87

A "Sensitive Plant"

Many plants, including grasses, legumes and a species of mimosa called the "sensitive plant," react to touch, heat or other stimuli by curling up and seeming to wilt. These movements are caused by sudden changes in water balance. The mimosa has a compound leaf structure: many tiny leaflets are symmetrically arranged along the forked lengths of each twig. Each leaflet is supported by a swelling at its point of attachment, and the twig shows a similar thickening where it joins the stem. These odd swellings are the "sensitive" organs: their thin-walled cells are supplied with water by fine loops of conducting tissue that connect with the plant's central plumbing system. A slight stimulus destroys the water balance in one or all of the swellings at the bases of the leaflets; a stronger one produces a similar reaction in the cells of the twig organ. Eventually the entire sensitive plant may be affected, as is demonstrated in these pictures.

REACTING TO TOUCH, the leaflets of a mimosa fold up when water stored in sensitive organs at their bases drains away, causing a loss of turgor. Next the twig droops as turgor loss affects cells in its base.

IN TOTAL COLLAPSE, the mimosa seems to writhe and wilt, its leaves tightly rolled. This collapse may take no more than a second, but the recovery of lost turgor is a process that may continue for hours.

Rain, the Life-Giver

No plant can live without water, and many can live and reproduce only in aquatic environments. Land-dwelling plants, in turn, depend primarily upon rainfall for this vital water supply. Thus, although temperature range, soil variety, length of day and other factors all play their part in determining what plants grow where, the most important single influence, as shown on these pages, is rain. The world's rainfall record—over 460 inches a year—is held by Mount Waialeale, Hawaii. At the other end of the scale lie the world's deserts, where entire years may be rainless and only the thriftiest plants can survive the long droughts between accidental showers. As annual rainfall increases in areas undisturbed by man, the grasses are the first plants to flourish: vast prairies, such as the Great Plains once were, dominate the scene. Next, trees—which in general require more plentiful water—appear in increasing numbers until, with abundant rainfall, the natural landscape becomes devoted exclusively to forests.

0 INCHES Extreme deserts, such as the Lower Colorado Basin area shown here, may be rainless for years at a time. Then a chance storm can unload tons of water in an hour and the seemingly sterile sands come to life, as long-dormant seeds bloom and produce new seeds to lie invisible until the next downpour.

25 INCHES The grasslands of our prairies, the Argentine pampas and the steppes of the Old World enjoy a thick protective cover of dead blades and roots that hold the scant moisture well. The grass may grow as tall as 10 feet in 20 to 25 inches of annual rain, but the dry winds do not favor the growth of trees.

35 INCHES An annual rainfall of 35 inches, the average along the U.S. coast from New Jersey to Florida, should permit development of an abundant forest. As shown above, however, water is not the only factor affecting vegetation. The region's sandy, leached-out soil supports little but scrubby stands of pine.

5
INCHES

The hot desert that extends from Mexico into the American Southwest seldom receives more than five inches of rainfall in a year. The water-thrifty plants of the area include the Joshua tree *(above)*. Sometimes mistaken for a cactus, this yucca is in fact a giant, skeletonlike relative of the lily family.

10
INCHES

The cold desert of the Great Basin, in Nevada and Utah, has a rainfall of as much as 10 inches yearly. Here, scattered growths of sagebrush dominate the landscape. These sturdy plants have taproots that probe deep for ground water, and extensive nets of shallow rootlets to absorb occasional rain.

45
INCHES

The forest that covers the Appalachian Mountains from New York to Virginia receives 45 inches of annual moisture, with winter snowfall accounting for as much as a quarter of the total. Birch and beech, ash, maple, hickory and oak are typical trees, with a mixture of conifers in the Northeast.

100
INCHES

The extravagant rainfall that marks America's wettest zone, the Olympic Forest in Washington, permits the growth of a dense tangle of conifers. Western hemlocks, red cedars and Douglas firs reach a height of 200 feet or more, while mosses and ferns flourish in the shadows of the forest floor.

WATER HAS BEEN REMOVED FROM SEEDS IN THIS TUBE BY CHEMICAL DRYING

Challenging the Future

Ordinarily, seeds can be stored for only one or two years before humidity makes them dissipate their store of energy and they will no longer germinate. Those with firm, hard coats retain their viability longest, and most seeds keep best in dry storage at low temperatures. Under such favorable conditions, seeds of common farm and garden plants have lasted from 10 to 25 years. Would they last longer if kept completely dry? Seeking an answer, Dr. Frits Went, author of the chapters in this book, launched an experiment in 1947 which is designed to continue for more than 300 years. Seeds of 120 California wild plants were chemically dehydrated in a vacuum and then the seeds of each species were divided among 20 vacuum-sealed tubes and stored in the dated jars shown on the opposite page. Since the start of the experiment, seeds from four sets of tubes have been germinated. The results: so far the test seeds have proven on an average to be as viable after 10 years' storage as they were immediately after drying.

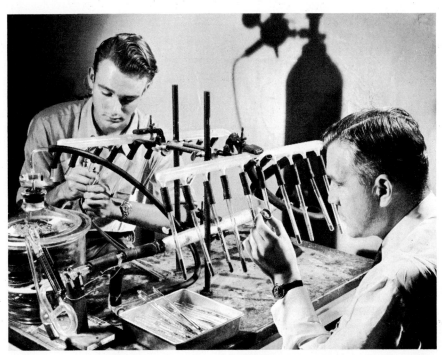

ARRANGING SEEDS for a test, Dr. Went shelves 20 identical sets (*left*) according to date of future use. From each tube, 60 to 100 seeds will be remoistened at a temperature of 65° F. to start germination.

DEHYDRATION COMPLETED, Dr. Went and his son Hans vacuum-seal the test seeds. Some seeds from each tube will be raised for future comparison of the revived plants with their wild descendants.

93

The Timeless Lotus Blossom

Under very unusual circumstances, the viability of some plant seeds can be preserved almost indefinitely. The record for longevity is held by the Oriental lotus, which has been proved by carbon-14 dating to have successfully survived centuries of dormancy in Far Eastern peat bogs. Oldest of all were three lotus seeds, recovered in 1951, which had been buried in a neolithic canoe 18 feet under a peat bog near Tokyo. Carefully tended by experts, two of the three venerable seeds germinated and developed their characteristic flowers, and innumerable seeds as well as cuttings from these plants have since been sent to botanical institutions throughout the world.

A 2,000-YEAR-OLD LOTUS SEED has its hard coat cut open by lotus expert Dr. Ichiro Ohga, exposing the embryo within. Placed in water, the revivified seed sprouted four days later.

HOW A LOTUS BLOSSOM OPENS is acted out by Dr. Ohga. On the first day, it resembled a sake bottle; on the second, a sake cup; on the third, a soup bowl; on the fourth, a saucer.

FULL-BLOWN PINK LOTUS, whose color Dr. Ohga predicted 14 months earlier, developed exactly like a lotus of today. After the fourth day, the petals turned brown and dropped off.

5

The Quest
for Clues
to Growth

ONE of the basic attributes of life is the capacity to grow. I do not mean the simple growth of a crystal, where preformed molecules dissolved in a surrounding liquid simply add themselves together, like rock sugar. True growth, as it takes place in plants and animals, is quite a different process, involving the production of entirely new molecules which arrange themselves very specifically to produce whatever kind of living organism the genes involved may call for. In true growth the pattern is *not* determined by the structure of the molecules; on the contrary, the same molecules (for instance, those of cellulose) may be arranged in very different patterns to produce anything from a blade of grass to a silver maple.

Growth in plants is slow, and to the casual observer a developing tree or flower may seem to be static, unchanging, with no visible growth movement whatsoever. This is only because we are accustomed to observing relatively fast movements; we need special devices really to see how plants move. Of course they cannot transport themselves from place to place, since generally, except for free-swimming algae, they are anchored by their roots in one particular spot; but despite this limitation, they do move in many different ways. Everyone who has ever seen a slow-motion movie of a growing plant shoot will recall how it continuously waves back and forth. Even older plants have very prominent daily movements, stretching their leaves out horizontally during the day, drooping or folding them vertically at night.

Nor are plants static in form—they change as they grow. A plant is different not only from season to season, but from seed and seedlings to fruiting, and from bud to blossoming. In fact, a plant really has four dimensions: the three which we see when looking at it, and a fourth one—time. The complete plant is a manifestation of a series of stages of growth. An acorn is as much an oak as is the majestic forest tree, and the leafless tree in winter is, botanically speaking, just the same as the tree in full leaf or in splendid autumn color—all are only time variants of the same species.

But not only is time in itself important to a plant. Another aspect of the same problem is *timing*, or time in relation to the plant's environment. This is beautifully expressed by the Japanese cherry trees along the tidal basin in Washington: they all flower simultaneously. In the same way, all the beech trees in a town leaf out on the same day. We are so used to seeing this that we seldom stop to think about it, but when we consider this phenomenon somewhat more closely, it becomes a major miracle. It is obvious that the trees in one part of town do not know what those in another part are doing. Nor do they live in exactly the same environments. Some may grow sheltered between houses, others may be exposed along a lake in the park, but all are synchronized when the moment to sprout leaves comes.

PERHAPS even more remarkable is that all the leaves on a single tree open on the same day. After all, the lower branches live under quite different conditions from the higher ones, and it seems almost inconceivable that branches on the north and south sides or the inside and outside of a tree should have been subjected to exactly the same conditions. Elsewhere we do not find such perfect timing: when we sow a bunch of seeds, all the plants do not appear at once; some may be days or as much as a week behind others. This variability might be expected in bud break too.

The precision of the timing in the bud break of trees suggests that it is under the control of two mechanisms. Since all the cherry trees in Washington open their buds at the same time, there is probably an external signal or influence at work. But since cherries usually bud a month before beeches, and since both species vary from year to year by a week or more in the time of their budding, it is probable that the external signal is a very complex one, different for each kind of tree. In some cases we know that it is connected with the amount of cold a tree has been subjected to in winter; in others it may be related to spring temperatures.

The second signal, which tells all the buds on one tree to do the same thing on the same day, must be an internal one. This signal achieves a degree of coordination comparable to that displayed by an organist using all 10 fingers and both feet to play a four-voice Bach fugue. In his case the coordination comes from a central nerve mechanism—the brain. But in plants there are no nerves, no structures of any kind along which impulses can be sent through the body to the extremities—which makes the problem of simultaneous bud break all the more fascinating.

To understand more about these timing mechanisms, we must first inquire into *how* a plant grows. We already know that growth in a plant starts with successive divisions of a fertilized egg cell to produce a blob of undifferentiated cells. These then differentiate into an embryo with a tiny stem tip, or plumule, one or two seedling leaves and the beginnings of a root. In most seeds, the embryo itself is very small, less than 1/25 of an inch long. The bulk of many seeds is taken up by the seedling leaves, or cotyledons, which have already developed into relatively large food storage organs. A peanut, once the shell and outer skin have been removed, reveals this structure clearly. The two halves of the individual peanut are the cotyledons, fitting neatly together like the halves of a sea shell and hinged at one end, where they are attached to the embryo. The tiny pointed object between them is the embryo, beautifully sculptured, ready to begin using the food stored in the cotyledons and grow into an entire peanut plant as soon as germination starts.

The first stage in germination is a general swelling, a taking in of water by the whole seed until each cell has absorbed enough so that its cell components can go to work. Once this is accomplished, the embryo can actually start growing. For about a week, water intake continues, but it is now no longer an indiscriminate swelling; instead it is concentrated in the rapid elongation of the young stem and the root. Pushing up toward the air and down through the soil, these two members lengthen without thickening. During this stage, the cells in the embryo, which were very tiny when formed, now become 10 to 100 times longer than they were. This is made possible by the delivery of a plentiful supply of sugar to each stem and root cell from the stored food in the cotyledons. Thus enriched, the cells can take up great amounts of water, which increases their turgor and literally stretches them—beyond the point where they can contract again, so that this growth is permanent. Since the structure of the cell walls is such that they can stretch only lengthwise, the plant does not grow like a baby, in many dimensions, but only longitudinally. It is like the one-way stretch of a pair of garters as compared to the three-way stretch of a girdle or a pair of stretch pants.

The cell walls of the seedling leaves, however, are built differently. They are so thick that they cannot stretch very much; therefore in spite of all the sugar they contain and their high turgor pressure, they cannot grow any more. All they do is supply the embryo with food, and thus the interplay between cotyledon cells and embryo cells, with their different stretch properties, causes the peanut to grow at a particular time in a very particular way.

How does a plant cell achieve this ability to stretch in only one predetermined direction? The electron microscope has given us the answer. Through it, we can see that one of the major components of cell walls is cellulose, long chains of sugar molecules securely fastened end to end, with practically no stretch in them. These cellulose molecules, grouped in tiny bundles, show up under the electron microscope as fine threads in the cell wall. They are imbedded in plastic pectin, which can stretch in every direction. But in cells which can only elongate, the cellulose bundles, or fibrils, are threaded through the cell wall crosswise, like the steel spiral in the hose of a vacuum cleaner. Just as the hose can be stretched in length but not in diameter, the cellulose fibrils effectively prevent the cell wall from increasing in girth, but do permit it to get measurably longer.

It is primarily by this kind of stretching that the cells of a tiny embryo produce a seedling. But for further growth new cells are required, and so it is that while existing cells are stretching, cell division is also constantly taking place,

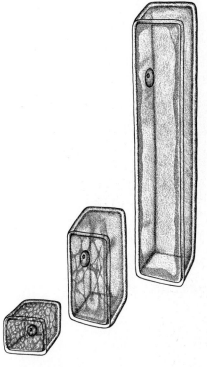

CELL ENLARGEMENT

All but the lowest plants are aggregations of cells, and no matter what special task each cell may ultimately perform, all grow in the same way: by enlargement. Starting with a fixed ration of protoplasm (color) within its walls (left), the cell begins its growth by elongation. Water is taken up into the vacuoles in the protoplasm, swelling them and stretching the cell walls (center). As the walls expand, the protoplasm is stretched farther and farther. Finally, the many, small, liquid-filled vacuoles combine to form a single large vacuole that occupies most of the cell's interior (right).

for the most part in the stem and the root tip of the little seedling plant.

The most delicate part of the stem is its very tip. This consists of small embryonic cells which divide continuously to produce more stem. Mostly they add to growth in only one direction, but every now and then they branch out in other directions to produce the first beginnings of leaves or flowers. The regularity of the cell divisions in the stem tip is astounding, for new leaves are formed at completely regular intervals so that they appear in regular patterns on the fully developed branch. A similar regularity is found in the production of flower parts.

Not until most of the cells of the mature stem have been formed in the stem tip do they start to elongate, first slowly, then accelerating to a maximum rate after a few days, and finally slowing down again to a complete halt. There is great variability among different plants in the speed at which stems grow. This is not due to different rates of growth in individual cells, most of which tend to double their size in a day, but to the length of the section of stem tip that is actually involved in the growing process. Among slow-growing plants, only about a quarter of an inch at the end of the stem does the growing. But among the fastest-growing stems, such as bamboo shoots, as much as two feet of the end of the stem may be involved in the growth process. A combination of cell division and cell stretching all along this two-foot growing zone can produce as much as a foot of new stem a day in bamboos. This enables them to reach their full size of 100 feet in only a few months, whereas 100 feet of growth in a tree might take several decades. The difference is not due to a faster growth rate of individual cells in the bamboo, but to the vastly greater number of cells that are all stretching at the same time. Also, while the shoots of most trees grow for only about a month each year, bamboo shoots grow without interruption, a prodigious feat requiring enormous amounts of energy food. This the bamboo keeps stored in a huge rootstock, replenishing it with sugars produced by photosynthesis in all the leafy shoots.

EVERY once in a long, long while—every 33 to 66 years, or every one or two human generations—bamboos in effect commit suicide. For reasons which we do not entirely understand (some say it is sunspots, but this is no more than a guess), the giant bamboos burst into bloom, sending up enormous flowering shoots which take the place of the ordinary leafy shoots. These flowers use up all the plant's reserves of food without in any way replenishing them, and the inevitable result of this spendthrift flowering is the death of the plant. In the tropical regions where bamboos provide the bulk of the building materials for native huts and many other structures, this is a calamity. Another curious aspect of this phenomenon is that all bamboos of the same species flower in the same year, regardless of where they may happen to be growing. A Javanese bamboo may be transplanted to Jamaica, but it will bloom at the same time as its brothers back home.

A most remarkable case of rapid development occurs in *Dictyophora phalloidea*, a tropical stinkhorn mushroom. It forms egglike balls, or "devil's eggs," in the humus layer of tropical forests. Inside each devil's egg lies a complete folded mushroom. Development starts in the morning, usually at about 7 o'clock, with the rupturing of the outer cover of the devil's egg. Then a blunt head emerges, covered with a liquefying mass of black, evil-smelling spores. In the next hour a stem unfolds, lifting the head four to five inches above the egg. Finally a beautiful lacelike white veil unfolds from under the spore-carrying

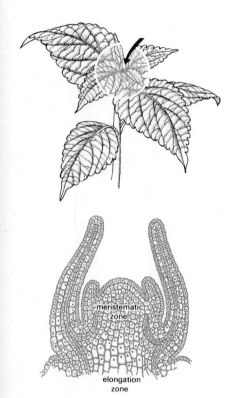

THE CENTER OF GROWTH

Some cells are able to divide throughout a plant's lifetime. These cells, located in key areas such as the tip of a stem, are the centers of plant growth. Shown here in an enlarged cross section (bottom) is the growing tip of the coleus plant (at top). The cells that divide are located in the central meristematic zone. As they multiply, they leave behind them a zone of elongation. Here the cells begin to increase in size, generally becoming from 10 to 20 times longer, through intake of water. These enlarging cells form a variety of different tissues as they mature.

head. This unfolding is completed in only a few minutes and it happens so quickly that photographs taken of it may be blurred because of the continuous movement of the veil.

When watching a growing plant, one soon becomes aware that its growth is strictly controlled. This is evident whether the plant be a large one or a small one, fast-growing or slow-growing. Big trees, in short, do not get big by chance. Clearly this is the outward and visible result of a growth-control mechanism of some kind. That the control is extremely strict is obvious—the cells of any stem must all grow at the same rate, for example, if the stem is to grow straight. If they do not, if those on one side grow faster than those on the other, the stem will become lopsided. Thus, in any plant, a high degree of coordination between the different growing parts is a clear necessity. One of the first scientists to become aware of the significance of such coordination was Charles Darwin. He demonstrated with experiments that the behavior of a young plant stem is directed by the growing tip at its end. Somehow the tip was passing instructions back to the stem below it. Darwin also showed that a root tip directs the response of the young root. Here, then, were two control centers, each directing the behavior of the parts under its "administration," so to speak. Darwin concluded that this control, although not the same, was comparable to that exercised by the brains of very simple animals.

T HE actual mechanism of the internal control of stem growth was discovered about 35 years ago. First found in grass seedlings, it later turned out to work the same way in the stems of most other plants. A grass seedling is a relatively simple structure. A sturdy hollow cylinder, or coleoptile, pushes up through the soil, enclosing the delicate young seedling leaves. When the cylinder reaches the soil surface, it stops growing and thenceforth acts as a protective tube through which the young grass leaves can push up without being injured by coarse sand or other soil particles.

If the tip of the coleoptile is cut off, growth slows down and, after a few hours, stops completely. This is not because any permanent injury has been done to the stem, but simply because of the absence of the tip. If the tip is replaced on the stump, the stem starts growing again. It will grow even if a thin layer of gelatin or agar is smeared between tip and stump. But when tip and stump are separated by an impermeable substance like a piece of tin foil, the stump will not resume growth. Clearly, therefore, growth is guided by something which diffuses from the tip to the stem. This can be proved beyond question by placing amputated tips on thin slices of gelatin or agar for an hour or longer and then placing only the agar on the decapitated coleoptile. The result is a resumption of growth just as if the tip were still attached, demonstrating that whatever it is that the tip provides the rest of the plant to make it grow has been transmitted to the agar.

Identification of this growth substance proved to be a long and tedious task. At first attempts were made to extract it from the coleoptile tips themselves, but this approach was abandoned when it became apparent that it would take 10 girls working 70 hours a week 70 years to obtain a single gram of the substance. Other approaches led finally to purification and crystallization of a growth substance from both animal and plant sources which was found to be identical with indoleacetic acid. This substance, also named auxin, and some others closely related to it proved to be phenomenal growth stimulators. One speck of indoleacetic acid diluted a millionfold in water could produce meas-

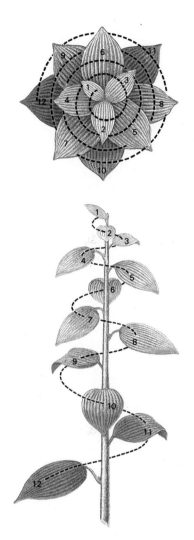

SHARING SUNLIGHT

Leaves in shady spots seldom shade each other—in fact, with mathematical precision, they are neatly spaced to give each other access to the sun. They grow in a spiral pattern, and if the spirals from the topmost leaf (above) are counted outward to the next leaf in the same relative position, the first part of a mathematical formula is obtained—in this case three spirals. Next, the leaves are counted, up to, but not including, the one in duplicate position: the total (below) is eight. These figures, expressed fractionally as 3/8, reflect the fraction of the stem's circumference between successive leaves.

urable growth in a coleoptile. From this it was possible to calculate that if all the growth that theoretically could be produced by a single ounce of auxin were placed end to end it would circle the earth. By comparison, one ounce of sugar has the potential to produce about a fifth of a mile of seedling growth, or only 1/100,000 as much as auxin. This shows that the auxin, unlike sugar, does not act as a building block in stem growth but is a hormone, a substance formed in very small quantities in one part of the body (the coleoptile tip) and transported to other regions (the growing parts of the stem) where it then proceeds to exert its effect.

Once auxin had been identified, it was possible to learn something about how it works. Being produced in the stem tip, it moves downward through the cells in the stem, stimulating growth in those that it is able to reach. But as the stem lengthens in response to this growth, the tip producing the auxin will get farther and farther away, and the supply of auxin filtering back will be increasingly reduced. Eventually the growing tip will be so far removed from the cells lower down in the stem that they will stop growing altogether.

Quite recently much interest has developed in a new type of plant-growth factors, collectively called the gibberellins. These are a group of chemically closely related substances which, like auxins, are a factor in stem growth, but unlike auxins can cause excessive elongation in a number of plant stems. Conversely, we know that lack of gibberellins may produce dwarf plants. This is particularly true in a number of dwarf varieties of peas, corn, beans and other garden plants. A row of dwarf corn, for example, which normally grows to a height of four feet, can be made to grow to the same height as normal corn by giving it repeated doses of gibberellin. Growth of normal corn plants, curiously enough, is not increased by gibberellin, nor does auxin, artificially applied, increase growth in dwarf varieties.

W E have seen now what a marvelous system of interrelating factors lies behind the seemingly simple matter of plant growth. Let us consider for a moment something that seems just as deceptively simple: how it is that plants grow straight up and down—as most of them do—invariably sending roots downward into the soil and stems upward to the needed light and air.

Our first reaction is likely to be a somewhat baffled: "How else would they grow? Sideways?" To which the botanist might justifiably reply: "Well, why not?" After all, when a seed falls to the ground it has no way of telling whether it is right side up or upside down; it gets buried any which way. How can it tell in which direction to send out its first rootlet and its tiny plumule?

To the plant embryo, the question is a vital one. It must extend its roots into the soil for water and nourishment; it must send its young shoot upward out of the soil into light and air. And the answer to how it manages this is the force of gravity.

There is no doubt that roots and shoots of plants are very sensitive to gravity. No matter how we plant and replant a growing root or shoot, it will adjust itself so that a few hours later the root is pointing downward and the shoot upward. This phenomenon is known as geotropism, which means literally earth bending. That this is a response to gravity can be demonstrated by experiment in several ways.

First of all, we can plant a seed and let it germinate in total darkness; when we examine the young plant that has grown from it, we will find the root growing down into the soil, the shoot reaching upward. We can then replant it

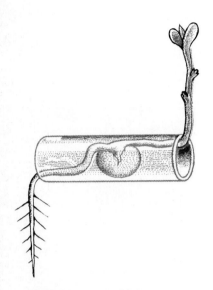

RESPONSE TO GRAVITY

When a seedling is grown inside a tube (above), its stem will turn upward and its roots downward as soon as they escape the tube's restricting walls. This reaction, positive for root and negative for stem, is known as geotropism—a response to gravity. The English experimenter Thomas Knight proved this more than 150 years ago. He fixed plants on a revolving wheel (below) so that centrifugal force counteracted gravity. The roots then grew outward and the stems inward, exactly as if gravity had been acting horizontally. This gravity response is now known to be induced by growth hormones.

upside down, and in a very short time it will adjust itself accordingly. Since this occurs in the absence of light, we can eliminate light as a factor and concentrate on gravity.

Now, if we fasten the plant to a turntable which rotates slowly on a horizontal axis, like a record player placed on edge, we get a different story. Here the plant is not subjected to the one-sided pull of gravity. On the contrary, what is up now will be down half a minute later, so that it receives no continuing stimulus to grow in any one direction. And sure enough, a plant growing on such a turntable will not readjust itself but will continue to grow in whatever direction its root and shoot were pointing when it was planted.

To prove our point still further, we can now speed up our turntable so that the plant will be subjected to centrifugal force which tends to pull away from the center of the turntable. When we do this, we find that the plant will grow in response to this centrifugal pull, with the root growing outward toward the rim and the shoot inward toward the center.

Once a plant has really started growing, with its shoot reaching out of the soil well into the open air, light becomes an important factor in its further development. Most stems are attracted by light, and it is possible to make a plant stem grow sideways by putting it in a dark room with a single light source at the side, as from a small window. This response to light is called phototropism, or light bending, and it, too, shows interesting responses in various plants and parts of plants.

Certain plant roots, for example, show a reaction to light by growing away from it, though most are unaffected. Certain leaves react very definitely by placing themselves as perpendicularly as possible to the light source so that they will receive a maximum amount of light. Thus house plants in a window tend to turn their leaves vertically toward the light that comes from outside. Some flowers lift their heads to face the sun fully, turning with it as it progresses through the sky. The leaves of the mallow, a common weed, do the same. When a tree trunk or some other object cuts off their view of the sun, they stop where they are, but as soon as the sun hits them again, they hurry to readjust themselves toward it. The most amazing reaction occurs after sunset: once the sun has dropped below the horizon, all the mallow leaves turn around and face east in anticipation of the sunrise that is still many hours away. It is almost as though they had a built-in intelligence telling them where the sun will reappear; but of course, they do not. More likely, this is just another manifestation of the 24-hour rhythm so prevalent in plants.

In addition to geotropism and phototropism, growth in various parts of the plant, particularly the roots, is also affected by the presence of water and nutrients, as we have seen in Chapter 4. Where there are layers of soil particularly rich in water, minerals or both, plant roots will tend to concentrate their spreading and growing in these layers.

How do plants turn in response to light or gravity? In most cases, such movement is the result of uneven growth of the stem— a more rapid development of cells on one side than on the other, which has the effect of literally bending the stem. Since auxin has now been identified as the principal factor in this growth, it would seem logical to suppose that gravity and light have some effect on it. Actually, auxin as a substance is not affected by either, but its movement from the tip of the stem or root where it is formed is very definitely affected. For example, in any plant that is not growing absolutely straight upward, gravity

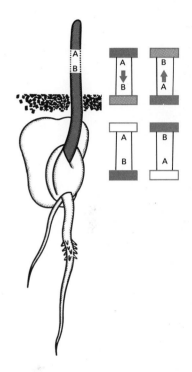

THE MIGRATION OF AUXIN

One of the unexplained properties of the growth hormone auxin is that it moves only in one direction from the plant tip where it is produced. A section (A-B), cut from a corn sprout, is placed between an agar block containing auxin at the top (A) and an untreated block at the bottom (B) (upper left). The auxin diffuses through the plant tissue from tip to base. Even when inverted (upper right), the one-way flow continues despite gravity. When instead the auxin-charged block is put at the bottom of the sprout section (lower left and right), no auxin diffuses whether the section is upright or inverted.

will cause most of the auxin to collect and flow along the leaning, or lower half, of the stem, stimulating growth on the lower side and righting the stem again. Also, light seems to deflect auxin away from it. Thus a stem that leans away from its light source—as a window plant that has been inadvertently turned around or a forest plant whose light has been cut off by a fallen tree— receives more auxin on the dark side. Cell growth is stimulated on that side, with the result that the stem will grow toward the light again.

From this it follows that we can explain the phototropic response of a plant in terms of auxin, but why light should tend to deflect the auxin still defies the scientist. This, of course, is one of the things that makes research so endlessly fascinating: each time a discovery is made which brings the scientist a step nearer to the ultimate solution, a new problem presents itself which must be solved in turn.

THUS far we have been concerned mainly with growth in length of stems. Once a cell has reached its final length in the first weeks or months of its existence, it does not elongate further and its cell wall becomes irreversibly rigid. Except for the upper few inches or feet of a plant, there is no further upward growth. This disposes of the old belief that initials carved in a tree trunk will eventually disappear into the higher branches. Actually, a nail driven into a one-year-old tree will always remain at the same height, and a sapling can be used as a fence pole or support for barbed wire without fear that the wire or fence will be lifted above its original height. The only further growth in a tree trunk is an increase in girth. If we carefully measure the circumference of a healthy tree, we find that some time in April or May it starts to increase. It grows most during the night, and toward the end of the summer stops again until the next spring.

All the growth in thickness of a tree trunk must obviously occur near the outer surface; the center, being solid wood, of course, cannot expand. It is equally obvious that the new growth cannot occur right on the surface—the young growing cells with their delicate, thin cell walls need the protection of the bark. Thus the dividing cells of a tree trunk or branch should be—and indeed are—located in a thin layer between wood and bark called the cambium.

Although it is responsible for all the lateral growth in a tree trunk, the cambium layer is almost unbelievably thin. It is, in fact, only one cell thick. Since it is located between wood and bark, it is only logical that the cambium layer should produce both—and it does. As it divides, it forms wood cells inwardly and bark cells outwardly. The steady production of wood cells slowly makes the trunk of the tree bigger and bigger, forcing the cambium layer and the bark farther and farther from the core of the tree. The newly formed living cells of the bark can adjust themselves to this expansion by dividing, but the dead outer layers of bark—the cork layers—cannot, which explains why the bark of many trees, like pines and oaks, is split into long cracks and ridges. In other species, like birches and sycamores, it flakes off in strips or patches.

Not only does the number of cells formed by the cambium vary according to season, but also the type of cells. In the spring the new wood is relatively soft, with many vessels in it, but in summer a much harder wood is produced with many fibers and extra-thick cell walls. This causes the grain in wood, which is clearly visible as a series of concentric rings when the trunk is cut crosswise. Reading from the center outward, a ring of softer, lighter-colored wood will gradually become darker and harder, then change suddenly into a ring of lighter color again. Each double ring of lighter and darker color corresponds to the wood produced by the cambium in one growing season. These are the so-called annual rings of a tree and they tell a detailed story about the climate during the years in which the tree grew. In dry years only a thin ring is formed, in years with abundant rain the rings are wide, and the pattern of sequences of wide and narrow rings is so distinctive that an expert can tell the year in which those particular rings were formed. In this way a chronology of year rings has been established reaching far back in time, and thus we have learned, for example, that after the year 1290 there was an exceptional drought in the American Southwest, which apparently forced the pueblo dwellers of Mesa Verde to leave their cave cities. This bit of deduction was made possible by the fact that the Indians used tree poles in the roofs of their dwellings, and since all the poles which have been preserved in the pueblo show by their ring patterns that they were cut before 1290, the evidence is clear that the Indians must have moved away at about that time.

No example of plant growth is more remarkable than the development of the pollen tube which a higher plant must have to achieve fertilization of the female egg by a male sperm. Plant sperm are produced in pollen grains. These are brought from male to female blossoms by the wind, by insects or by birds, depending on the species of plant, and deposited on the sticky surface of the styles, the stalks which grow from the female parts of flowers. Once this contact has been made, a pollen grain begins to produce a threadlike tube which grows down through the center of the style in the direction of the egg cell lying in the ovary at the bottom. The male nucleus then descends this tube and impregnates the egg cell. Considering the small size of the pollen grain, the length of the tube it produces is almost unbelievable. In corn the pollen tube has to grow through the silk and the whole length of the ear toward the egg cells, a distance sometimes as much as a foot. And yet the pollen grain from which this tube grows is only one thousandth of an inch in diameter!

We have learned a good deal about plant growth by studying fast-growing plants and observing the roles played by hormones, gibberellins, water and nutrients. Now let us see if these insights cannot be sharpened by looking at some slow-growing plants. What we learn is that if light, water and nutrients are in short supply, then the plant will be stunted. That is most obvious among some plants growing in sand dunes. There both water and nutrients may be lacking, and consequently the plants are dwarfed.

WHAT about plants that are deliberately deprived of the things they need? This is the secret of bonsai, the Japanese art of growing dwarf trees. Every possible trick is used to inhibit the growth of these plants—cherries, cedars, maples. In their natural state all of these would be many feet high, but they are carefully deprived of nutrients, pruned of their fastest-growing shoots and buds, kept in small pots with reduced root systems, and they respond by turning into miniatures of themselves, with tiny leaves and twisted little trunks—their growth almost, but not quite, brought to a standstill. The smaller they are, the more gnarled their trunks are and the more tortuous their branches become, the more effectively they suggest age and the more highly they are prized. Some of these bonsai trees are more than a century old. Theirs is indeed life at its lowest ebb.

Another aspect of the time problem in plants is the length of their life span. This may be as short as a few weeks (as in desert annuals), but usually it is longer: about half a year in the case of most annuals; two years in biennials such as carrots, beets and foxgloves; or an indefinite number of years in such perennials as the iris and peony, and in shrubs and trees. In some cases, such as lichens, which grow so slowly on rocks in the polar regions, or the bristlecone pines of the California mountains, it may be thousands of years.

The difference between annuals and perennials is, of course, that when an annual dies at the end of the year, the whole plant expires forever. It has done its job, grown seeds and scattered them, and the continuation of the species will be attended to by new plants sprouting from seeds in other places. The shriveled stem of the old plant has no further use; it dries and disintegrates. Perennials, on the other hand, make use of old growth. Much of the structure of a tree is dead, such as the cork and the center of branches and trunk, but it continues to fulfill a purpose. Each year's new growth adds to the strength and thickness of the trunk and extends its branches a little wider and a little higher. But this growth is accomplished by only a tiny percentage of a tree—the growing tips and the cambium layer. These continuously dividing meristems must stay alive and grow seasonally, putting out new shoots and fresh leaves and flowers every spring and increasing the trunk and bark. Thus, whether it be a fragile violet with a life expectancy of only a few months or a California redwood with an expectancy of thousands of years, a plant must keep growing. When it stops growing, its days are numbered.

THIS is one of the basic differences between plants and most animals. When an animal reaches maturity, growth stops. Bone and nerve cells cease to grow and divide. Other cells merely replace themselves without increasing the size of the individual. An animal, once it reaches its proper adult size, can exist that way for a long time without further growth. The reason for this is that although some of its cells—bone, brain and nerve—are not replaceable, they have a long life, and the animal machine can get along with the same ones for years. Eventually, however, they will wear out and the animal will die. Plant cells, by contrast, have a shorter life and must be constantly replaced. Maple or sycamore leaves formed in April drop off and die in October. In live oaks the leaves grown one spring drop off the next spring immediately after a fresh crop of leaves has been formed. They do this even in climates where there is no cold winter, as in the case of the southern magnolia and the holly. It is the life span of the leaf cells themselves and the replacement rhythm of the tree—not the temperature—that causes them to fall.

Among conifers the needles are longer-lived. In many species they last for two years or more, and in the slow-growing and almost ageless bristlecone pines of the lofty western mountains, needles may live as long as 20 years. Theoretically, in fact, plants ought to be immortal—there is no reason we know of why an Italian poplar tree, for instance, could not be perpetuated forever through cuttings, which continuously produce new trees. Nevertheless, the individual plant does have a definite age limit, although we now know, because of the work with bristlecone pines, that the age limit is at least as long as 4,600 years. To that extent, at least, trees are closer to immortality than man. But true immortality exists only for undifferentiated cells or single-celled organisms which can continue to divide ad infinitum. Thus a bacterium may be said to be half a billion years old. But men and plants have followed the path of differentiation and specialization, and both must in the end pay the price of their complexity with their mortality.

FULL OF LIFE, THREE ACORNS PUT OUT ROOTS WHILE A FOURTH LIES EMPTY, HAVING BEEN PIERCED AND ITS INSIDES EATEN BY AN INSECT

Forces That Drive Plants

Although most plants are stationary, none are ever static, for their growth calls for movement. Whether spiraling upward, bending to light or responding to the tug of gravity, they are under the control of a hormone called auxin, which, along with other hormones, also influences many other plant activities. And when at last they come to fruition, they often send their spores and seeds flying.

COMING TO FRUITION, a cellular slime mold shows the spontaneous movement inherent in the growth of even the simplest plants. Made up of undifferentiated cells which have flowed together in a prelude to reproduction, it first begins to form a

PHOTOTROPISM, the response of plants to light, is shown in time-lapse photographs of a fast-growing fungus. The plant oscillated between two light sources as it spiraled upward.

Plants in Motion

Motionless though they may appear to be, plants actually are moving continuously. Most of their movements result from growth, and it was Charles Darwin, in the 19th Century, who first discovered that growing parts of plants, including their roots, describe a spiral as they elongate. The rate of spiraling varies considerably throughout the plant, of course—it is great for a tendril but much smaller for a root.

Growth movement is internally controlled, but other plant movements, the tropisms, are brought about by external stimuli. Thus stems and leaves bend toward light. The leaves of a vine growing on a stone wall, all tipped at right angles to the light, become a mosaic, overlapping little, each presenting as much of its surface to the sun as possible. Gravity stimulates the vine itself to grow upward while sending its roots downward. And the climbing movement of the vine along the side of the wall is in response to the stimulus of contact with the stones.

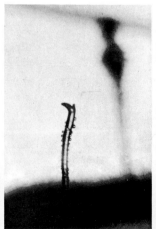

GROWING VERTICALLY, the young fruiting body of *Pilobolus kleinii*, a fungus that shoots spores at light, changes course by bending over when a light is shone on it from the left. Behind it in silhouette, a mature fruiting body, complete with swollen

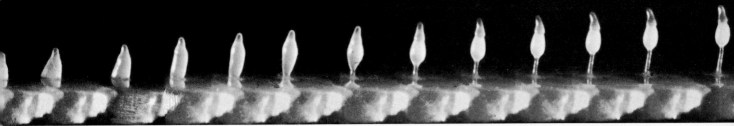

stalk, which appears as a bump on its side. The lengthening stalk next lifts a ball of cells to its tip. This ball develops into

spores and rises higher as the stalk continues to elongate. Thus the spores are finally brought into position for dispersal.

GEOTROPISM, a plant's response to gravity, is shown by oat seedlings photographed every 10 minutes. The one in the middle is kept upright, but the flanking pair are placed hori-

zontally. The effect of gravity redistributes their growth hormone to the undersides of the sprouts so that growth is accelerated there, causing the seedlings to point upward again.

stalk and terminal spore case, bends directly to the light, taking aim. Fired with force, the spores stick to grasses and are

swallowed by herbivorous animals, which carry them to new locations in their dung, a natural medium in which they grow.

The Telltale Curves of Growth

Of the many factors that work together to make a plant grow, one of the most important is the hormone called auxin, produced in the leaves and wherever cell division is taking place. Auxin not only promotes growth; it also, in so doing, controls a plant's response to light and gravity. The "*Avena* test," devised by Dr. Frits Went and reproduced on these pages, dramatically shows auxin's influence. When young shoots of *Avena*, the common oat, have their tips cut off, growth ceases. By affixing to the headless sprouts tiny blocks of agar into which auxin has diffused from the amputated tips, growth can be restarted in the cells in one side—and the angle of growth that results (*opposite*) is a measure of the amount of auxin that seeped into the test block.

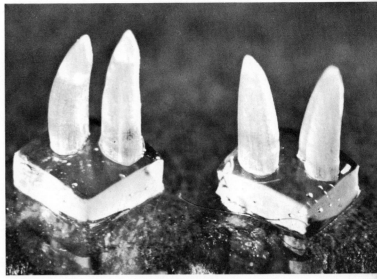

DECAPITATED TIPS of oat seedlings stand on blocks of agar as a first step in the *Avena* test. Auxin, the growth hormone that is produced in the tips, is now diffusing into the blocks.

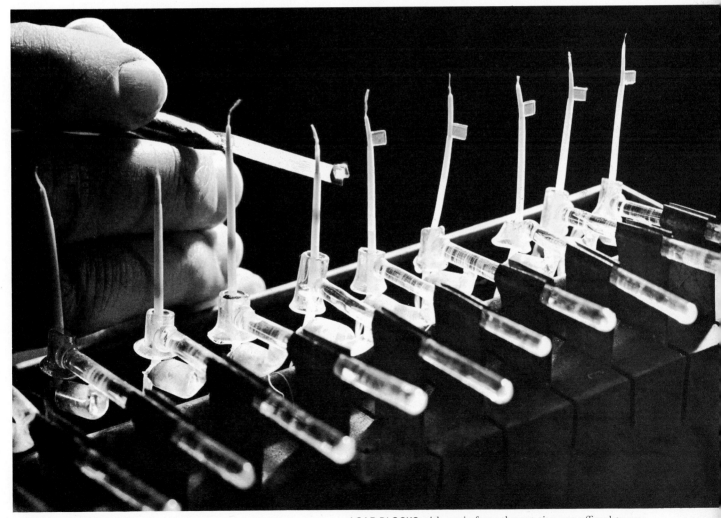

CURVING PROGRESS of the seedlings, 100 minutes after the test began, shows that auxin, transmitted from the agar, has restarted growth, but only on the side where the blocks are.

AGAR BLOCKS with auxin from the oat tips are affixed to one side of each seedling in step two of the test. The blocks rest against the central leaves, exposed when the tips were cut off.

Hormones: Keys to Plant Control

A plant develops as a unit because each of its key parts produces hormones needed by at least one other part. Roots would fail to grow were it not for the vitamin B_1, produced as a hormone by the leaves of most plants. Stems, no matter how much auxin they receive from buds and leaves, would stop growing if roots were unable to supply them with another hormone called factor X. Thus hormones—not sugar, as is often supposed—control the extent to which a plant will grow. Hormones also govern such processes as the dropping of leaves or fruit. Scientists have discovered that spraying apples with auxin keeps them from falling prematurely from the trees, and spraying mature cotton plants with antiauxin causes the leaves to drop off, making it easy to pick the bolls.

WHY LEAVES FALL is shown here in an experiment with a *Coleus* plant. Two

THE ROLE OF AUXIN in root production is demonstrated in an experiment with lemon cuttings supported by a wire mesh. The two slips at left, which had their leaves cut off, have failed to put down roots. But the two slips at right, from which the leaves were not removed, have developed them fully—the leaves were able to supply the auxin needed to initiate root growth.

leaf blades have been cut off, leaving their petioles, or leaf stalks, with no source of auxin. One petiole is then daubed with auxin. Thus supplied, it stays firmly attached to the plant —but the other petiole falls off when its auxin level declines.

THE ROLE OF VITAMIN B₁ in root growth is shown in the different development of these Camellia slips. The two at left have been given auxin, which has stimulated some root growth. The other two have been treated with both auxin and vitamin B₁, and as a result their roots are much more luxuriant. Normally, Camellias would get B₁ in sufficient quantities from the soil.

BURSTING ITS SEED COAT, a piñon pine seedling puts down its first root.

The Awakening Embryo

The germination of a seed, so often regarded as the beginning of life, is to a plant actually only the resumption of growth. For the seed contains an embryo, an incipient plant which had its first development on the parent plant. Once separated from the parent, it must wait, often through a long dormancy period, until outside conditions are exactly right to start growth on its own. This occurs when the seed takes in moisture, reactivating its protoplasm. Enzymes come into play, digesting starch

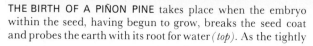

THE BIRTH OF A PIÑON PINE takes place when the embryo within the seed, having begun to grow, breaks the seed coat and probes the earth with its root for water (top). As the tightly packed seedling leaves, or cotyledons, elongate and swell with moisture, they force off the coat and are hoisted from the ground by the lengthening stem (bottom left). The endosperm

to sugar and converting other materials into growth factors. Respiration increases, energy is released and the cells of the embryo begin to elongate. The first part of the seedling to emerge is the root, which anchors itself in the soil. The second part to appear, the sprout, differs in its growth pattern from species to species. In the bean, for example, two seedling leaves, or cotyledons, come out of the ground on the stem, but in the pea they stay underground as the plumule, or apical bud, pokes up.

SPREADING ITS LEAVES, the piñon seedling is now completely on its own.

still clinging to the cotyledons provides nourishment and will soon be discarded; the cotyledons themselves, unlike those of many other plants, do not contain stored food. In the photo-graph above, the plant at left has its cotyledons unfurled, while its partner is still straightening up, and is on the way to becoming a full-fledged tree, capable of growing 20 to 35 feet tall.

115

From Flower to Seed

Beautifully varied though they are in color and form, all flowers still share the same structural plan, designed in all for the same end—seed production. The typical flower, in addition to its base, has sepals and petals that form its cup, and in the cup are stamens and a carpel, with its ovary. The stamens make pollen in the anthers at their tips, and the ovary produces ovules.

When a pollen grain lands on the carpel's stigma, it germinates and forms a pollen tube, which slowly grows down through the style into the ovary, bursts through the wall of an ovule and discharges its car-

UNFURLED, THE POPPY'S PETALS RADIATE FROM THE OVARY AND STAMENS. ONCE FERTILIZATION HAS OCCURRED, THEY FALL AWAY. THE OVARY THE

THE TIGHTLY PACKED BUD of a red poppy, clasped shut by its two hairy sepals (*left*), breaks open when the folded petals inside begin to enlarge. The sepals, breaking loose from the stem, cling to the expanding petals, become yellow and eventually fall to the ground. In the last photograph, the deeply creased but fully formed petals still shield the stamens and carpel, the male and female organs of reproduction.

go of twin sperms. If the ovule is to develop into a seed, fertilization must take place not once, but twice: one sperm must fuse with the egg nucleus to form the embryo, the other sperm with the so-called polar nuclei to form the endosperm, or nutritive tissue. In many plants, the embryo is smaller than the endosperm, but in such plants as corn and the other cereals, the embryo draws upon only a portion of the stored food, reserving the remainder for early seedling growth. As the seed or seeds develop, the ovary enlarges into a fruit, which may become fleshy or grow into a dry capsule, like the poppy's below.

ROWS BIG WITH MATURING SEEDS AND FINALLY DRIES OUT. HERE, PART OF ITS WALL HAS BEEN CUT AWAY TO SHOW THE SEEDS PACKED INSIDE

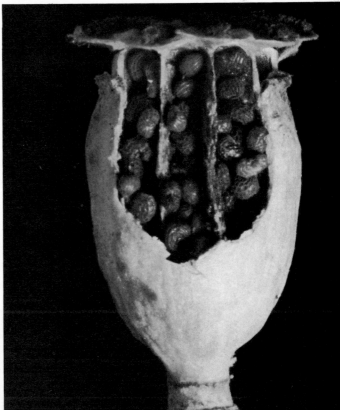

A DANDELION CLOCK, shown with only a few of its seeds, forms its spherical shape from the flat base of the flower, which curves in drying, positioning the seeds for dispersal by wind.

Parachutes and Spitting Pods

Seeds are dispersed by many agents, including the wind, water, animals and even the actions of parent plants. Some seeds, like the million-odd produced by an orchid, are so small and light that a breeze is sufficient to waft them on their way. Others have specific structures to aid their dispersal—everything from the tiny parachutes of the dandelion at left to the hooks and spines of beggar's-tick, cocklebur and stickseed. Some are forcibly ejected. The witch hazel fruit, splitting open slowly, squeezes its slippery seed between its moist halves and sends it skidding forth. Touch-me-not and jewelweed have seed pods which swell as they mature; when the pods finally burst, the ripe seeds inside are hurled out.

OLD-MAN'S-BEARD produces feathery seeds which flutter through the air. The plumes (*above*) are formed from the style, part of the carpel, which is discarded in most other plants as seeds develop. The tufts found on dandelion and thistle seeds are also formed from flower parts, but those of milkweed are not—they are silky outgrowths of the otherwise hard seed coat.

LOOKING LIKE INSIDE-OUT UMBRELLAS, SEEDS OF GOATSBEARD ARE BLOWN BY WIND TO NEW LOCATIONS

6

The Molding Force of Climate

LIKE any living organism, a plant has a certain individuality, determined by its genetic constitution, molded by its environment and developed by the conditions under which it grows. Plant breeders know this, and it is by no means pure affectation that leads them often to speak of their tulips, roses or African violets in the same terms that pet lovers use for their cats and dogs. For they have taken infinite care to obtain the best varieties and they baby their plants along from bulbs, seeds or cuttings to a perfect flower or fruit. This is actually what a "green thumb" is. The term might more appropriately be "green mind," indicating a mind which understands what plants need for their best growth—the right kind of soil, the proper amount of water and the most suitable temperatures and light. For it is the interaction of all of these environmental factors with its own particular genetic character which determines how a plant grows.

Some plants even seem to have "feelings." The aptly named "sensitive plant" of tropical America, which grows in unshaded moist spots, in meadows or in clearings, is the most extreme example of this—when touched or handled roughly, its leaves close as though they were afraid of injury. Possibly this is a protective mechanism to prevent their being eaten by grazing animals; certainly their sudden drooping, which is caused by an abrupt change in turgor in cells at the joints of leaflets and leaf stalk, makes them look unpalatable. And their reaction to what we in human terms would call shock is remarkable to see: if a burning match is held under the tip of a leaf, not only will that leaf immediately close, but in rapid succession all the other leaflets along the leaf stalk will close too, and then, more gradually, the main joint reacts, and finally the stimulus moves slowly up and down the stem itself, causing a general drooping. It is almost like watching, in extremely slow motion, the transmission of a stimulus along the nervous system of an animal.

But, of course, we know that plants do not have nerves and consequently do not feel pain or have any emotions whatsoever. They respond directly to light, gravity, temperature, moisture, chemicals, surrounding plants and animals. They seek the light, rise in the wind's eye, straighten or bend according to need, orient roots and stems as gravity dictates, and search out nutrients and water in the soil. They adjust themselves to their surroundings. Irrevocably rooted in one spot, they have to take rain, wind, winter frost and summer heat as they come. Much more than animals, they must adapt themselves to the particular conditions of the area in which they grow.

THE soil, of course, is an important factor in the environment of the plant. Soil is a most remarkable material. It is incredibly complex in its mineral and organic content and its microbial and animal composition, with earthworms, gophers, grubs, nematodes and many larger animals burrowing into it; with rain, decaying vegetation and still other animals constantly depositing new materials upon it. No two soils are really identical, yet all good topsoils have a number of highly beneficial qualities in common. They are able to hold large quantities of water—up to 20, 30, 40 per cent or even more of their weight —and they can store plant nutrients, releasing them to plant roots upon demand. Nitrogen, phosphorus, magnesium and potassium may be thus stored in great quantities in the more fertile soils, and at the same time there will be minute quantities of the so-called micronutrients—iron, zinc, copper, manganese, molybdenum and boron—the trace elements, as they are known, which are required only in the smallest traces.

The natural vegetation of any locality is usually adapted to the water and nutrient supply of the particular soil which is present there. Good soil will support quite intensive cultivated crops too; but when man tries to force the utmost out of his cultivated fields, the demands on the soil become too great, and natural water and nutrients must be augmented by irrigation and fertilizing. In this way the soil can be effectively managed and changed to suit the plant's and the grower's requirements.

The most important fundamental factor in a plant's environment, however, is not soil but climate. If we pause a moment to think of what we actually mean by climate, we may soon conclude it is an unsatisfactory term. Climate is nothing concrete; it is an abstraction. It is the average weather in a particular locality, and we know how utterly unreliable and changing the weather can be. The climatologist may calculate from the weather records of a particular area that it has a wet summer and dry winter, with an average summer rainfall of 20 inches, but neither he nor anyone else can possibly say how much rain will fall on a particular day or even in a particular month. Temperature is just as unpredictable and even more changeable. Every day the temperature rises and every night it drops considerably again—a situation so complex that meteorologists express it as an average daily temperature, or a maximum and minimum. But a plant does not respond to an *average* temperature—with no ability to control its own temperature, it reacts to the temperature actually prevailing. Since, as we will see, a tomato sets fruit only when the night temperature is around 65° F., an *average* temperature of 65° will usually not permit fruit production; and it would depend on the *difference* between day and night whether an average temperature of 70°, 75° or even 80° would be satisfactory.

How do we find out what specific climatic conditions a plant prefers? We can, of course, grow plants in different localities and see how they behave. But this does not help us very much; no two years are the same with respect to weather, and in one year a plant may do twice or even four times as well as in another year. In 1955, for instance, when New Jersey had an unusually hot summer, average tomato production was only 2.9 tons per acre, whereas in the previous year it had been nearly twice that. California is one of the few states with a relatively stable summer climate, and consequently California shows a relatively stable record of tomato yields.

But even the performance of tomatoes in California cannot tell us just which aspects of the climate are most conducive to high fruit production. This can only be done in a laboratory in which all climatic conditions, including temperature, moisture, light and wind, are under control. When I grew tomatoes under precisely controlled climates where I could maintain cooler or warmer summer, spring or autumn conditions, I was able to confirm that temperature was the crucial factor in their growth—but only the temperature during the night. If it rose above 75° F. or fell below 60° F. at night, no tomatoes were formed at all. Production was high only when night temperatures ranged between the narrow limit. Therefore in a hot summer, such as that of 1955 in the East, commercial tomato production is certain to decline.

Night conditions are also critical for the production of potatoes. Unless the temperature is around 53° F., potatoes do not produce enough tubers to be commercially profitable. This, of course, makes it difficult for a grower to produce potatoes and tomatoes simultaneously on a commercial basis: when the night temperatures are just right for tomato fruit set, they are not right for the formation of potatoes, and vice versa. This explains why Maine, Idaho and Ireland, with their cool summers, produce excellent potatoes, while California is the major tomato-producing state.

MANY people tend to think of frost as the great climatic dividing factor between plants: tropical plants are those which are killed off by frost, Temperate Zone plants are those which can survive it. Actually, plants are much more subtly adjusted to temperature than that. The African violet is an excellent case in point: it does not grow well unless kept warm, especially during the night (70 to 75° F.), and it will die at around 50° F., long before frost temperatures are reached. The troubles of an unsuccessful African violet grower, in fact, can usually be diagnosed as open windows at night. I myself divide American flower lovers into two categories: those who can grow African violets and all others who cannot—and these same two categories are equally sharply divided into those who sleep with their windows closed or open at night. For the opposite reason, English daisies and other spring flowers cannot be grown as house plants: they die when they are kept too warm.

Gardeners make good use of the differences in climatic requirements of flowers

IDEAL TEMPERATURES FOR RAISING PLANTS

Of the many factors that affect plant health, optimum day and night temperature is one frequently ignored by amateur growers. The temperatures listed below are most favorable to flowering and fruit set for eight popular plants.

PLANT	(DAY) HIGH	(NIGHT) LOW
African Violet	73° F.	65° F.
Petunia	83° F.	61° F.
Zinnia	80° F.	65° F.
Stock	61° F.	55° F.
English Daisy	60° F.	48° F.
China Aster	75° F.	60° F.
Tomato	75° F.	65° F.
California Poppy	65° F.	50° F.

to keep their plots in bloom. Heat-requiring plants like zinnias and petunias are grown in the middle of summer, whereas cool-temperature plants such as stocks and pansies are grown in spring. Roses are the ideal garden plants: they grow and flower at any time of the year, except winter, because they are tolerant of both warm and cool weather. Roses may be seen in gardens all over the world, from Alaska to the Amazon, but there are few other plants that have such a wide range of temperature tolerance.

THE tropics, of course, would seem to be an ideal place to grow plants, with favorable temperatures 12 months a year. Curiously enough, however, most deciduous trees and shrubs from temperate climates do no better in the tropics than do their tropical counterparts in the cooler zones. The same is true of spring-flowering bulbs like daffodils, tulips or hyacinths. For the first season they may seem to do well, but after they have lost their leaves and flowers they go into a sort of winter sleep from which they simply do not awaken again. Keeping pear or peach trees over the winter in a heated greenhouse is similarly fatal to them. All of this points up a most interesting aspect of the effect of cold on these Temperate Zone plants: they need it, though in a different way, just as much as tropical plants need warmth.

The fact of the matter is that these deciduous trees and bulbs have to go through a certain amount of cold after they have lost their leaves in autumn before they can awaken from dormancy and start to grow again. Only by exposure to cold can they be apprised of the end of winter. If this seems a backward way of doing things, consider what would happen if springtime warmth were the only factor in reawakening them. An unseasonally warm month in midwinter could cause them all to open their buds prematurely, only to have them frost-killed for good when cold sets in again. It is a most extraordinary protective mechanism that prevents this, one so finely adjusted to the local winter climate that an eastern variety of peach, for instance, accustomed to cold winters, cannot be grown in Florida or California, while a California variety will almost certainly be killed in the Northeast because its dormancy will be broken by a warm spell before the winter is over.

The spring-flowering bulbs are a particularly graphic example of this temperature-control system. During the summer, when temperatures are high, the newly produced bulbs of tulips and hyacinths form leaves and flowers for the next spring. If they are dug up then and gently pulled apart, these will be clearly visible inside the bulb. But these newly formed leaves and flowers will not emerge from the bulbs before they have spent some time in a very cool temperature, such as they might experience in winter. That is why we tuck them away in a cool part of the house or cellar before bringing them out to flower again. Similarly, most of our early spring-flowering trees and shrubs have leaves and flowers formed and ready to open in the fall, neatly folded in bulb or bud, some of them from August on—but it takes the double signal of winter's cold and spring's first warmth to trigger their opening. Just what the chemical mechanisms involved in this quite marvelous phenomenon consist of, we do not know; there may be some inhibitor which is gradually broken down by cold, but if so, it still awaits discovery.

Clearly, temperature differences explain much of the distribution of plants all over the world. Climbing a mountain illustrates this graphically: the whole range of temperatures from tropical, subtropical, temperate and subarctic to arctic is experienced in hiking up a mountain in the Peruvian Andes or New

Guinea from sea level to 16,000 feet. It is like traveling 5,400 miles from the equator to the Arctic Circle. From the tropical vegetation on the coast the climber passes at mid-altitudes into the oak forests, and then encounters the conifers higher up. Finally, he is confronted by a tundralike scene a thousand feet below the areas of eternal snow.

The final change occurs here at the timber line, above which no tree grows. This is not a matter of altitude, but simply of cold. In the tropics the timber line may be anywhere from 13,000 to 14,000 feet up; in the California Sierras and the northern Rockies at 10,000 to 12,000 feet; in the Alps at 6,000 feet. In New Hampshire's White Mountains it is around 5,000 feet and in southern Alaska only from 1,000 to 3,000 feet up from the sea. From the timber line on, there is a limited area of tundralike vegetation with hardy grasses, mosses and dwarf shrubs. Then, in arctic temperatures, only occasional lichens are found on exposed rocks which get above the freezing point often enough to enable these hardiest of all plants to survive.

Together with temperature, the other great fundamental factor which molds the vegetation of the earth is water. One quarter of the land area of the world is arid or frigid—too dry or too cold for plant growth. Another quarter is semi-arid, permitting only sparse vegetation—vast, treeless areas of steppe and semi-desert, covered with hardy grasses, sagebrushes and other low shrubs that can get along with a minimum of moisture. The remaining half of the earth receives enough rainfall and warmth from the sun to have a good plant cover—and under natural conditions, most of this land would be covered with forest, as it was before man came.

Whenever temperature and moisture are even halfway favorable, the plant cover tends to become a forest. Where there is an excess of water, however, as in lakes and bogs, no trees can grow—with two exceptions: mangroves and swamp cypresses. The adaptations which these two types of trees have made to secure a proper balance between air and water are most interesting.

Mangroves are found along all tropical coasts where mud flats are periodically flooded by the tides of sea and ocean. There is no oxygen at all in the mud, and since the roots of all plants require oxygen for growth and functioning, they have had to evolve some way of bringing oxygen to their roots. All the trees of the mangrove vegetation have done this, generally in peculiar ways. The most common mangrove tree, *Rhizophora*, produces stilt roots which emerge from the trunk above the high-water line so that they can take up air at all times. Others, like *Sonneratia*, have a spreading root system, with the main roots running horizontally through the mud and a series of upright roots emerging above the mud and water. These have a spongy structure full of air channels through which the roots buried in the mud can breathe.

The swamp cypress, *Taxodium*, common to the swamp areas of the southern United States, has perhaps evolved a somewhat different system. It has peculiar "knee-roots," humpbacked portions of the main roots running through the mud which at fairly regular intervals come above the water. These knee-roots have air channels through which the rest of the root may absorb oxygen. Other characteristic plants of swamp areas, like reeds and rushes, get air to the roots through their stems—in the case of small shrubs, their root systems are poorly developed, which results in slow and stunted growth.

Of all the forests in the world, the tropical jungle and rain forests are the richest in species. Why this should be is difficult to explain—the conditions of

A DOUBLE LIFE

Myriophyllum, a fresh-water plant, has two completely different kinds of leaves—one for use above water, the other for use submerged. The aquatic leaves, longer and narrower than the aerial ones, provide a maximum surface for the assimilation of dissolved gases. Tossed by the current and continuously changing their position in relation to the light, the water leaves have upper and lower surfaces undifferentiated in structure. The tops and bottoms of the aerial leaves, however, show different structures and have guard cells and stomata. They also show a much greater proportion of woody tissue, which is needed for support.

competition are so extreme that one would expect that only relatively few species could have developed and survived. Yet it is typical of a jungle to have as many as 100 or 200 different species of trees growing together in a vast, wild and seemingly patternless tangle.

In one way, this is a good thing for jungles—it protects them from man. The dozen or so species of economically valuable trees are so widely dispersed in the exuberant wilderness of useless vegetation that it is almost prohibitively expensive to cut and remove them. No such wholesale deforestation as Europe and North America have known is likely in the Amazon basin, for example—as the business of getting wild rubber has shown.

At the turn of the century, the wild rubber trees in South American jungles were virtually the only source of rubber in the world, and far up the Amazon great riches were to be had, exemplified by the booming cities of Belèm and Manaus. The rubber bleeders were a rough lot, men who penetrated into the heart of the jungle in dugout canoes, miles from civilization, seeking out the scattered rubber trees. Their tapping methods were crude and exhaustive; they generally injured the trees, which dropped in productive capacity, forcing the tappers deeper and deeper into the wilderness in their search for more trees. It was a method of exploitation which could not last, although the Brazilian government protected it as long as possible with stringent laws against the exporting of rubber plants or seeds. When rubber was finally successfully cultivated in plantations, after seeds were smuggled out to Malaya and elsewhere, the Brazilian wild-rubber industry was practically put out of business, and a severe economic slump in the Amazon basin followed.

In the drier tropical regions, the forests are less exuberant and rich in species, with the monsoon and thorn forests chiefly characteristic of these areas. India's teak forests belong to the former category—during the dry season the trees shed their leaves and the area takes on the appearance of a winter scene. The thorn forest, or caatinga, of the state of Ceará in Brazil grades into a thorn shrub vegetation with all further transitions to desert, where the yearly rainfall drops to a dozen inches or less.

I N the temperate regions, the forests are less rich than in the tropics, with usually 10 or even fewer species of trees. Most of the natural temperate forests are mixed hardwoods and conifers. An appallingly large percentage of all temperate forests has been cut, either to clear areas of land for cultivation or as a source of lumber. This in turn has necessitated planted forests, with a resultant monotony of species. In Europe there is hardly any natural forest left, and even in the United States rich stands of natural mixed forest like those of the Appalachian Mountains are dwindling.

Australia has a completely different type of forest, with eucalyptus the main component and some acacia intermixed. It is a remarkable fact that one genus can so completely dominate a continent. Different species of eucalyptus grow from the coastal areas to high up in the mountains, from cool Tasmania to the tropical Northern Territory—low shrublike mallee, giant karri and mountain ash. The latter, covering the mountains of eastern Victoria, belong to the most beautiful and majestic forests I have ever seen.

The most impressive forests in the world are doubtless those of the sequoia in California, but other parts of the world also have their giant trees, some with diameters of dozens of feet. The kauri trees (*Agathis*) of New Zealand are gigantic, and so are the *Fitzroya* of southern Chile. The next largest were per-

A HORTICULTURAL COMPASS

Prickly lettuce, a weed found in Europe and the United States, grows with its leaves aligned to the east-west path of the sun. Viewed from east or west (drawing at left), it appears to be a broad plant, but viewed from north or south (drawing at right), it is revealed as a flat one. This flat growth pattern allows the prickly lettuce to catch sunlight full-on through most of the day.

haps the cedars of Lebanon, now almost completely gone, and the cedars of the Atlas Mountains in northern Africa. Strangely, all these giant trees are conifers, a class of plants which are now being overshadowed in number by the flowering plants. One is tempted to think of other giants, the dinosaurs, now long since vanished from the earth; but the giant conifers certainly are still around, even though man is decimating them.

In the colder regions of the Northern Hemisphere, pine, spruce or fir forests replace the hardwood or mixed forest. Usually a few broad-leaved trees such as aspen and birch are intermixed, producing a riot of color in autumn, when their golden yellow contrasts with the somber green of the conifer foliage and the blue of the sky. Still farther north the trees become shorter and ragged; with dead tops or dying branches, they seem to be really struggling in the increasingly inhospitable surroundings. Finally they give way to a low shrubby vegetation of willows, and at last only the tundra remains. This final zone extends until the very soil is permanently frozen scant inches below the surface even at the height of summer. Beyond this no plants grow.

I N all the preceding pages we have seen examples of plants which needed very specific and specialized climatic conditions and therefore grew only in a limited range of localities. Are plants not able to adapt themselves to a different climate; can we not acclimatize them?

The question is not easy to answer: plants have their adaptations, but they are ingrained in the plant and do not change. Fur-bearing animals produce a heavier coat or longer hairs in winter; deciduous trees lose their tender leaves. Changed to a warmer climate, a deciduous tree will still lose leaves. Conversely a tropical plant without periodic leaf drop does not become deciduous when planted in a temperate climate. No matter how long and how often we try to change these habits, the plant remains unchanged. The response mechanism of a plant can be changed by the environment to only a very limited extent, and certainly not enough to enable the plant to grow in a very different climate. This limited adaptability of plants also limits their successful cultivation outside their native habitat.

However, man is not powerless against such inflexibility of plant responses. He does not have to submit to the limitations of climate and plant behavior. With the new tools given him by science and technology, he has any number of possible means to break this specificity of climatic adaptation. We have already seen how the mobility of man resulted in the spreading of rubber beyond its country of origin. Since the first voyages of Columbus, many other plants, such as corn, potatoes and tobacco, have spread from the Americas to Europe, Asia and Africa, and wheat and peas have crossed the seas in the opposite direction. But all this was relatively simple to carry out, entailing merely a matching of old plants to new localities with similar climates.

Today far greater possibilities are open to man to grow what he wants or needs. If the local climate is not right for a particular plant, he can change the climate, either locally or generally. He can also try, often very successfully, to change the response of plants to climate by deliberate selection or breeding programs. He can adjust the growing period to the most favorable temperature regime in a special locality, or he can find another climate in which the essential temperature and other characteristics are similar to the native country of the plant.

The first of these possibilities, a local change of climate, has been used almost as long as man practiced agriculture. Lack of rain water can be made up by irri-

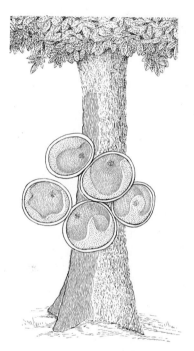

A CRUDE WAY TO FIND NORTH

The belief that moss on trees indicates the direction of north is defective in two particulars: the growth is not a moss but a green alga and points north only in an approximate way. A one-celled alga (inset), Pleurococcus, colonizes the side of a tree that is best shielded from the drying sunlight. It is true that this is most often the north side, but the growth is too broad to indicate a precise direction.

gation. Excessive winds can be curbed by windbreaks. Damaging low temperatures during the day can be offset by growing plants against southward-facing walls. Finally, of course, there is the greenhouse. In wide use by the 17th Century as a device to keep plants from freezing to death by placing them in a room with a stove, it was soon improved with glass roofs to furnish light and solar heat. Greenhouses were next equipped with ventilators to keep them cool in summer, and today horticulturalists are fully able to reproduce all manner of climates in greenhouses with the aid of air conditioning.

Curiously enough, it was not until 1933 that the first greenhouse was successfully air conditioned. It had not been recognized that enormous quantities of air were needed to remove the heat produced by the sun's radiation in a greenhouse. Today many commercial greenhouses have air conditioning, as do some research greenhouses and even a few used for display. The most remarkable of these, the Climatron at Shaw's Garden in St. Louis, encloses several different tropical climates within its single dome-shaped roof of plexiglass.

Climate control through greenhouses, of course, is only feasible for high-priced crops such as flowers and certain fruits and vegetables. If we want to grow staple food plants we cannot change the climate, but we can try to change the plant. How successfully this can be done is evidenced by such hybridized species as tomatoes, corn, wheat and many others which now can be grown over a much wider range of climates than was formerly possible, because a different response to climate has been bred into them.

WHAT still awaits us in further developing the potentialities of the plants of our world? Until a decade ago, we only considered plants and animals in an earth-bound environment. Today, the possibility of other life existing in outer space has moved from science fiction writing to serious speculation. Is it possible that, far removed from the limitations of the environment we know, there may be plant life similar to our own?

Any attempt to answer such a question must first of all consider the actual limitations placed on life as we know it on our planet. Of all the existing temperatures in the universe, from hundreds of degrees below zero to millions of degrees above, there is only the range of about 30° to 120° within which active life is possible. We can survive at slightly lower temperatures only by artificially keeping our body heat up; plants can do so by closing up shop and suspending life, and a very few bacteria and primitive algae can live in hot springs, but not above 180° F. This narrow range makes either the hot inner or the frozen outer planets doubtful sites of plant life.

As far as air is concerned, we could do without free nitrogen, but for animals and man any decrease of the oxygen concentration to less than one half is fatal. For plants, the critical oxygen content is about one quarter of normal. But plants could not possibly exist without carbon dioxide in the air. Since the atmosphere of most outer planets seems to consist largely of methane, it would appear impossible for plants to live on them. In addition to this, green plants need light— when this drops to less than 1/100 of normal sunlight, they cannot exist any more. This is another count against the outer planets.

It is not likely, therefore, that space exploration will bring us much new knowledge of plant life as we know it here. However, within even that relatively restricted space on our earth which is fit for life, the biosphere, there is still much to learn about plants, their potentialities and their peculiarities, as the following chapters will show.

A TROPICAL POOL EDGED BY PLANTS FROM AMERICA, AFRICA AND THE EAST INDIES MIRRORS THE MAN-MADE SKY OF ST. LOUIS' CLIMATRON

The World under Glass

Unlike most other living organisms, plants are literally rooted in their environment. If lifted from it, they cannot change their adaptations; unless they find the climate of their homeland, they will die. To grow them in captivity, for research, pleasure, food or commercial use, man has reproduced nature in many ingenious ways, even to artificially creating several climates under one roof.

THE CLIMATRON AT NIGHT seems to float like some ethereal bubble, its green vegetation gleaming beyond the dark lily ponds at the main entrance to the Botanical Garden. Under its 70-foot dome, plants crowd half an acre of ground. The tallest trees, like the balsa of the South American rain forest, reach almost to the apex. There, twin clusters of lights revolve

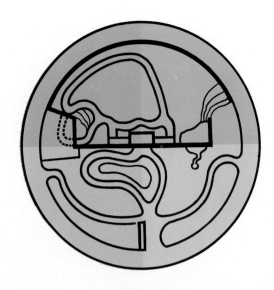

FOUR MAJOR CLIMATE AREAS are shown here on a plan of the Climatron. The dark blue area, like Java's mountains, has cool days and nights, with high humidity. Light blue marks a drier climate, as in India. The damp heat of a rain forest is shown in green. Darker green shows the cool days and warm nights of the Pacific. Temperatures range from 60° to 90° F.

A Harmony of Light and Habitat

Conceived and built by Dr. Frits Went, the Climatron in the Missouri Botanical Garden in St. Louis is the successful realization of a long-cherished dream of botanical scientists—to grow plants from several different environments side by side under controlled conditions. Beneath a roof of one quarter inch plexiglass, supported by a geodesic dome, the Climatron shelters more than 1,500 different species from tropical and semitropical areas, ranging from the damp heat of the Amazonian jungle and Hawaii's cool ocean climate to the dry tropics of India and the mist forests of Java's mountains. Its several climates are created by two ventilating systems drawing fresh air through many large fans. Controlled by a computer console which operates a complex battery of switches, the fans inhale and expel air according to outside weather conditions and the daily passage of the sun, while fine spray nozzles add humidity where it is needed. By night, the Climatron is lit by a simulated sun and moon. While its extraordinary beauty has attracted visitors in the thousands and won it an architectural prize, it is as much a tool of research as a display case, offering scientists a unique opportunity to observe exotic plants in various tropical climates and conduct experiments which normally entail months overseas.

at night, one casting brilliant sunshine, the other the pale light of a tropical moon. This dramatic illumination is also useful for the study of plant growth under varying light conditions.

131

A JUNGLE BOG, accurately reproducing the Amazonian climate, also shows the unrelieved and varying shades of green
characteristic of the area. Water lettuce covers the tiny pond
like a velvety carpet. In the left foreground hangs the large,
shiny leaf of a philodendron plant; beyond it is a cascade of
wild bananas (*page 137*) with leaves three feet long. Framed in

the center background is an African dragon plant with spiky leaves; above it droop the branches of a fig tree. Almost lost in the foliage of another philodendron species at the extreme right are the small leaves of a young jungle giant, the *Hymenaea courbaril*. This slow-growing locust will eventually become a sizable tree: its wild mates are an important source of timber.

A ROSE OF CHINA glows brilliantly yellow and red in "Little Hawaii." This Asiatic hibiscus is a variant of the normally rose-red flower, which now has been bred in white, buff and other shades. Some 200 species of hibiscus grow worldwide in tropical and temperate zones.

THREE FEET DOWN in a tropical pool, the stems and young, still-furled leaves of water lilies are silhouetted against the dim green of algae-rich water. Above, sunlight is refracted at the edges of floating lily pads. Visitors observe this aquatic scene from a plexiglass tunnel.

A TROPICAL FIG TREE coils its roots among the leaves of a jungle floor. This Australian species, *Ficus columnaris*, is frequently known as a "banyan" because it drops aerial roots from branches to the ground. Sometimes epiphytic, here it was planted directly in the soil.

A STUDY IN BROWN AND GREEN, two epiphytic ferns hang in harmonious coexistence. The big Australian staghorn forms deeply forked leaves, spreading six to eight feet from its central nest, almost hiding the small-leaved sword fern below.

A FLOURISH OF PINK, blooms of the wild banana, *Musa rosacea*, peep from their cluster of huge leaves. As the pink bracts fall away, the flowers become exposed and their ovaries swell into banana fruits. With scant pulp, these are barely edible.

FOREST SCAVENGERS, these pale fungi thrive on a rotten log, breaking it down into food by freeing nutrients. These will be used by the tiny green liverworts (visible behind the fungi) during their growth.

7

Climbers, Clingers and Predators

THE idea that plants, like any living thing, have particular places in which they prefer to live, and even particular plants with which they live congenially in communities, may seem a paradox. No plant, after all, can exercise a willful choice as to where its seeds may fall and germinate. Wind-borne, bird-borne or carried in water or by mammals in their fur, seeds seemingly face a haphazard distribution. Yet there can be no doubt that particular plants grow only in particular places, whether these be the rock to which some lichen clings, the treetop to which some climbing vine laboriously makes its way, or even, as in parasites and semiparasites, a host which provides them with what they need.

Nor is there any doubt that they live in specific communities which have definite boundaries. All of us have often seen how abruptly a forest gives way to prairieland or meadow. Experienced berrypickers know without thinking much about it that blackberries are to be found in hedges or at the edge of a forest, and wild strawberries elsewhere. If I need a ladyslipper orchid for a classroom demonstration, I look for it in very special places in the woods.

Part of the reason for this apparent choosiness of plants lies in their particular requirements of light, moisture, temperature and soil condition. But if their distribution depended only on these factors, many species would be far more widespread. As it is, we find upon examination that the undergrowth in a forest of pines, say, is entirely different from that in a forest of hardwoods, and when we analyze these differences in more detail, patterns of definite plant communities emerge. Each such community, characterized by its own special grouping, shows half a dozen or more species which always grow together, with a limited number of other species associated with them. And, as in the case of forest and field, the boundaries between the communities are usually sharply drawn.

The reasons why plants grow together in communities are only partly known. One interesting aspect of the matter is that there are certain plants which definitely inhibit others—in a plantlike way, they are antisocial. Some of these simply replace near neighbors by winning in the competition for water or nutrients in the soil. Others engage in a sort of chemical warfare by excreting substances which discourage growth in other species. Several desert plants do this, notably the rubber-producing guayule of Mexico, which excretes cinnamic acid from its roots. This substance is poisonous for other plants, so the guayule grows all alone. Similarly the black walnut spreads through the soil around its roots a poison which keeps other plants away.

MORE pleasant to contemplate are plants which help other plants to grow better. Clover is a well-known example—bacteria which are encouraged to grow in its root nodules fix the nitrogen of the air to produce nitrate fertilizer, which profits not only the clover but any other plant in the neighborhood. This is why clover and other members of the leguminous family are often planted together with other seeds, as in lawns or new gardens, or planted for the first year in poor soil which a farmer hopes to reclaim.

But, the perspicacious student may ask, what about botanical gardens? Here one finds thousands of different kinds of plants from all parts of the world and all varieties of conditions growing together with no apparent difficulty. How is this possible?

The answer, of course, is that it is hard to grow all those plants together and they are nurtured meticulously by man. Bogs, forests, meadows and ponds are created to produce a far greater variety of conditions in a smaller space than one might find in nature—but let the caretakers turn their backs and nature will soon reassert herself. Weeds will appear, natural competition will take over, and in the course of a few years many of the introduced plants will disappear entirely. A botanical garden will prove that plants can be made to grow outside their natural range, but it also proves that only by controlling the natural competition can such growth be maintained—and even then, the alien plant may be at a disadvantage, growing more slowly, flowering less abundantly and producing few if any viable seeds.

It might be logically assumed that all the plants growing together in a natural community are beneficial to each other in some way and to some degree. However, there are also associations which are quite one-sided. The most extreme case is true parasitism, in which one plant may live entirely at the expense of another. Many plant interrelationships are relatively harmless, but others can cause the death of the host.

Among the less harmful types are those remarkable climbing plants, the lianas, and the erroneously named air plants, the epiphytes, both of which use other plants as stepladders or platforms to enable them to obtain sufficient light for growth in an environment dominated by tall trees.

Lianas are particularly interesting because of the methods they use to climb up into even the tallest trees. One species ascends by twisting its stems around any suitable support, reaching up higher with every turn. This is the way the bean and the wisteria climb. Cucumbers, passionflowers and peas, by contrast, use tendrils—modified stems or leaf stalks which coil themselves around any support, somewhat like the prehensile tails of monkeys. Once they have found a hold, they cling tightly to it, and the tendril between coils up on itself, literally pulling the plant up so that new tendrils can form and reach even higher.

A good many lianas climb with the aid of thorns, which simply hook into anything that promises support. Roses and rattans climb in this fashion. In rattans, which are really climbing palms with very flexible stems (hence their use in the making of wickerwork), the thorns grow on a long, whiplike extension of the leaf stalk and are recurved. If this whip does not connect with a support, it will end up hanging down in the forest to the detriment of any careless traveler, for the sharp thorns can cut deep gashes in his skin.

Eventually, of course, the supporting tree may die, and then the lianas climbing on it will fall with it. Because of their very flexible stems, however, they usually survive the fall to send new shoots back up into other trees. Sometimes lianas which are not sufficiently anchored in a tree will slide down, leaving their stems all tangled and bent, a major obstacle to movement in the tropical jungle.

Lianas are a constant source of trouble, rather like an unruly pet, to the curator of a tropical botanical garden. Since they are an interesting part of the forest, he will plant young lianas once his trees have reached sufficient size, then proudly label them. For the first five or 10 years the leaves and flowers of the lianas remain reasonably close to the name plate, but in the end they may be hundreds of feet away, the stem having coiled its way from tree to tree, sometimes climbing in the crowns, sometimes falling down and restarting.

THE epiphytes, the second group of plants living in the trees, do not climb at all. They germinate high up and live there, not as parasites, but only to get a place in the sun. Most epiphytes are found in the moist tropics, and much of the crowded appearance of tropical rain forests is created by mosses, ferns, orchids and other epiphytic plants growing on the trunks and branches of trees.

Although it may seem simple enough for a small tropical plant to escape the deep shadow of the forest depths by using the branch of a tree to grow upon, the problems for an epiphyte are tremendous. Very few of them develop long enough roots to reach the soil; all others must live on such water and nutrients as they can find high up in the trees. In some cases, birds distribute the seeds by eating the berries produced by the plant and depositing the undigested seeds on the branches in the trees. But the majority of them have either very light spores, as in the mosses and ferns, or very light seeds, as in orchids and bromeliads, and these are distributed by wind. A single seed pod of an orchid may contain as many as three million seeds, a fact which gives at least some of them a chance to become lodged on a tree branch.

Once they have germinated, epiphytes face the further problem of hanging on and getting food. It is not surprising, therefore, 'to find many adaptations among the epiphytes for this special and precarious way of life. Many of them are succulents, with internal water reservoirs in the form of water-storage organs and tissues like the swollen stems, or pseudobulbs, of orchids and the thick leaves of *Peperomia*. Others have developed external water reservoirs, like the bromeliads, relatives of the pineapple, which have flaring leaf bases that act as

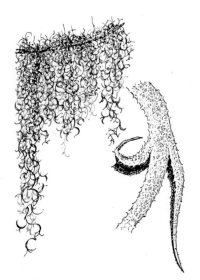

SPANISH MOSS AND DETAIL OF SHOOT

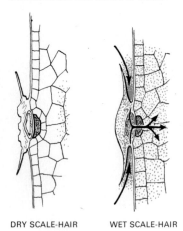

DRY SCALE-HAIR   WET SCALE-HAIR

A THIRSTY EPIPHYTE

The rootless tendrils of Spanish moss possess special structures that serve to absorb rain. These are tiny winged scale-hairs which cover the slender shoots (detail above) of this epiphyte. When no moisture is available, the dry air-filled cells behind these scales (cross section at left) are shrunken. The runoff of rain, however, is caught between the hair of the scale and this cell layer (external arrows in cross section at right). From here it seeps slowly into the plant stem (interior arrows) providing the Spanish moss both with water and with a ration of minerals washed from the host plant.

cups to catch and store rain water. These bromeliad water reservoirs are so effective that other plants and animals have become dependent upon them. Several tropical American aquatic insects, for instance, are found exclusively in large bromeliad cups. The cups are also a favorite breeding place for mosquitoes. (During the building of the Panama Canal one essential measure to combat malaria was to get rid of all bromeliads near construction sites.)

Perhaps the most peculiar adaptation of all is that of *Dischidia rafflesiana*, an epiphyte with long twining stems precariously attached to branches by a few roots. Along with its regular leaves, this plant also develops large leaf pitchers with which it gets both water and nutrients. Each pitcher has an opening where it is attached to the stem, and into this opening the plant sends a root which branches inside. Some of the stocking-shaped pitchers hang down and catch rain water; others, turned upward, remain dry and become a home for ants, which build nests in them. The refuse in the ant nest is, of course, an ideal source of food, and so the plant gets both nourishment and water from its self-grown feeding station.

A number of other epiphytes actually collect humus in their airy perches. One of these is the nest fern, which forms a rosette of very large leaves with the shape and function of a basket. Smaller leaves from the branches above are collected in this basket as they fall, and in time they produce a mass of humus so large that even earthworms live there. In Java, earthworms two feet long are not uncommon in the humus of nest ferns.

A more complicated variant of the humus basket is produced by the staghorn ferns (*Platycerium*). They live as epiphytes, attached to trunks and large upright branches, and they form two types of leaves—one broad and upright, with its base pressed against trunk or branch and its wide edge flaring out; the other narrower and green with chlorophyll, standing out from the host branch. The broad leaves soon die, remaining as a basket for humus collection; the narrow green leaves photosynthesize and produce spores for reproduction.

ONE of the most successful epiphytes is the so-called Spanish moss—a total misnomer, since it is neither Spanish nor a moss. It is actually a bromeliad, and it festoons trees in the tropical and semitropical Americas. It has none of the adaptations just described for a successful epiphyte. It does not have water-storage tissues and it does not collect humus. It has no roots of any kind. It looks more like ravels of gray carpet left to decay on the branches of the host tree. Yet Spanish moss (*Tillandsia usneoides*) covers more trees than any single other epiphyte. It gets all its water from rain. Its stems and leaves are covered with shieldlike hairs pressed tightly against them, and these take up any water under them by capillarity. The water is then absorbed by the plant through cells shielded by the hairs. This results in a perfect valve mechanism: liquid water can get in, but hardly any water vapor is lost.

There is still another advantage to this mechanism. When rain begins, the first water that washes down into the Spanish moss from the branches above is rich in minerals derived from cells of the host plant which have died. Thus the Spanish moss is abundantly supplied with nutrients in concentrated form. Furthermore, by the time the rain water has washed away the minerals and runs pure, the plant is already saturated and does not take up any more. This explains why Spanish moss is most abundant on old host trees with a large proportion of dead or dying branches and cells. The Spanish moss does not, as is so often believed, kill the branches on which it grows; on the contrary, it proliferates only when the host tree already has an abundance of dead cells.

The roots of many epiphytic orchids have a peculiarity all their own. Their outer cells are empty and filled with air. Their roots look thick and grayish-white when dry, and any rain water is absorbed as quickly and as thoroughly as if they were blotting paper. As soon as the root gets water, it turns green. The reason for this strange color change is that when rain water replaces air in the outer layers of root cells, they become translucent, and the chlorophyll-filled cells underneath become visible. Like the Spanish moss, these orchids also get a supply of nutrients from the rain, which washes minerals from the branches above.

By contrast to the lianas and epiphytes, which are only seeking sunlight, parasitic plants live off other plants and are counterparts of the many parasites found among animals, such as the microscopic malaria parasite or the tapeworm. There are many degrees and types of parasitism, from innocent-appearing eyebright and Indian paintbrush to the giant *Rafflesia* and the deadly dodder, which are completely dependent on their hosts. Some of the semi-parasites would never be suspected of parasitism at all—their predation is all accomplished underground, where they send out roots to connect with roots from neighboring plants, drawing unknown but presumably small amounts of food from them. The Indian paintbrush thus preys upon its neighbors, although with its green leaves and roots it looks fully capable of supporting itself.

Mistletoes, on the other hand, are true parasites, although at first glance they may seem to live like epiphytes. Their several species grow in temperate and tropical regions, germinating and living entirely on the branches of trees and shrubs. However, they have no true roots at all, and so they penetrate into the plumbing system of their hosts with rootlike processes, tapping the water which they cannot otherwise obtain. The Temperate Zone species do little or no damage to their hosts, but in the tropics it is a different story. There the water drain of mistletoes is often so severe that the host plant is killed.

One tropical tree, however, has a novel means of defense against the predations of the mistletoe. This is a spiny variety of the kapok tree, which in its smooth-branched form is subject to particularly severe attacks by mistletoes. The spines do not discourage the mistletoes themselves, of course, but affect the carriers of their seeds, the birds. Birds are very fond of mistletoe berries, and the seeds pass through their digestive systems intact, to be deposited with their excretions on the trees. Most mistletoe berries have a single seed inside, covered by a sticky glue which makes the seeds adhere not only to any branch they may encounter, but also, when they are excreted, to the feathers of the birds. Birds get rid of them by scraping them off against the trees—all but the spiny kapok, which discourages them from thus disposing of the sticky seeds.

There are a number of flowering plants which are total parasites, with neither chlorophyll nor true roots. Some, like dodder, or "devil's sewing thread," have long, slender, twining stems which encircle the host and penetrate its stalk. Their stems form dense mats around the attacked plant, often literally draining it dry. In stark contrast to dodder plants are the broomrapes, which parasitize clover, alfalfa and other cultivated plants. When their tiny seeds fall close to the roots of a host plant, they germinate and attach themselves to these roots, free-loading on the food, nutrients and water laboriously gathered by their host. The young broomrape plants grow rapidly into thick stems, which appear above ground as fat inflorescences from three to eight inches high. They

MISTLETOE "ROOTS"

AN ARBOREAL PARASITE

Although it is a parasite, the mistletoe contains chlorophyll and undertakes limited photosynthesis. Thus the plant supplies itself with at least some portion of its food requirements. But for water and mineral salts it depends entirely upon its tree host. To obtain these substances, the mistletoe has rootlike processes that develop along its stem wherever it comes into contact with the tree. These are known as haustoria, a name which is derived from the Latin verb "haurire," meaning to drink. Two of the mistletoe's haustoria are shown (lower illustration) as they penetrate the outer layers of a tree branch.

do not have to skimp on building materials: these are free for the taking, and while the broomrape thrives, the clover host plant is starved. A severe infection of a clover or alfalfa field with broomrape is a serious problem for the farmer, resulting in drastically reduced yields.

The most remarkable family of parasitic plants is mostly tropical. These are the Rafflesiaceae, named after the largest flower in the world, *Rafflesia*. In the Far East, in Malacca, Sumatra, Java and Borneo, a number of species of this genus parasitize a particular liana, *Tetrastigma*.

Rafflesia are rare and hard to find, as I can testify from my own experience. I had heard, when I was in Java many years ago, that *Rafflesia* were to be found on an offshore island named Nusah Kembangan (literally, the island of flowers). This was in 1929, when it was a penal colony for major criminals. My driver on this occasion was a convicted murderer, and my guide was serving time for cannibalism. These men took me into the depths of the jungle, hacking a path with heavy machetes. We found the *Rafflesia* at last in an opening between the trees: a huge brown and purple flower, almost two feet in diameter, spread on the ground. A few yards away was a large, brown, cabbagelike ball. This was the flower bud of another *Rafflesia* that would open in a few days. The open flower looked and smelled like rotting meat and was covered with hundreds of flies, crawling all over it, carrying pollen to the stigma and fertilizing the plant.

T HE greatest number of parasites in the plant world are found among the fungi, which, with their thousands of parasitic varieties, outnumber by far the few hundred parasitic flowering plants. Parasitic fungi are responsible for some of the most destructive of all plant diseases—for example, the Irish potato famines of the late 1840s were caused by *Phytophthora infestans*, which blighted crops for three years in a row. More than a million Irish died, hundreds of thousands more fled to America, among them the great-grandfather of President John F. Kennedy. Another fungus disease, wheat rust, was for untold generations a constant threat to wheat harvests everywhere. No effective countermeasures could be devised, until at last it was discovered that the source of the infection lay in a particular reproductive stage of the fungus, which arose only after it had passed a stage of sexual reproduction in a second host plant, the barberry. Eradication of barberry plants was the first effective step in controlling the disease in temperate regions, but wheat rust still remains a major agricultural problem.

Fungus diseases in most cases can be quite easily recognized because at some stage the spores themselves or the threadlike hyphae are visible on the affected plant. Mildew on roses, for instance appears as a whitish web over the leaves. Rusts become visible when their yellow, orange or black spores are formed in thick masses on the leaves or stems of infected plants. A number of wood-rotting fungi make their presence known when they sprout mushrooms.

Bacteria can also cause plant diseases—potato and tobacco wilt, for example —but a high-powered microscope is needed to find these tiny parasites. Another group of plant diseases, among them tobacco mosaic, which produces mottled and worthless leaves, is caused by viruses, organisms so small that they can be seen only with an electron microscope.

Scarcely less varied and widespread are the relationships of plants with animals—particularly those with insects, some of which are as important and fascinating as anything in nature. And among the insects it is those with the highest order of social organization—the bees and the ants—which have developed the

THE VARIETY OF GALLS

From root to crown, all plants are subject to the odd excrescences called galls. These lumps and warts, results of abnormal growth, are of five basic sorts, each produced by a different causative agent.

Nipple galls are produced by the insect called the jumping plant louse. Here they cover a hackberry leaf. Unlike many other galls, these are uniform in size and shape —each measures 1/6 of an inch across.

A black knot gall, triggered by a fungus, grows over the twig of a cherry tree. During its two-year growth to maturity, the velvety gall turns black, hard and brittle and may end up as a two-foot-long knot.

closest ties with plants. Bees are the great pollinators. Many ants accidentally or deliberately grow plants, perhaps the best-known being the leaf-cutter ants, which cultivate a special fungus on the mulch of leaves stored in underground chambers. There are other close relationships between plants and ants. Harvester ants collect seeds, which they store in their nests, often climbing into plants to pick them. In the tropics, there are other species which cultivate "ant gardens" on the branches of trees. Generally, these are made up of an ant nest overgrown by epiphytes. These epiphytes are all plants with oil-containing fruits, which are collected by ants for food. The seeds germinate in the nest, and the roots of the epiphytes help to anchor the nest. Thus the ants are provided with food and security while the plants are not only distributed but also supplied with humus and nutrients.

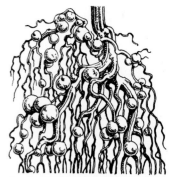

Some galls, like those covering the roots of this clover, are associated with a virus strain. Unlike insect-induced galls, those which a virus causes may vary in size and number from one plant to another.

A much stranger association is found in certain tropical plants which have developed structures specifically adapted to accommodate ant colonies. Some of them, such as *Cecropia* and *Triplaris*, have hollow stems in which ants live. This is not accidental, for the plants have developed special thin spots on their stems which ants can pierce to gain access to the hollow space within. Some *Cecropia* even develop small growths at the base of their leaf stalks, which provide food for ants. Still stranger is the case of a Mexican shrub, *Acacia cornigera*. It has developed large, hollow spines at the base of its leaves in which ants live. At the tip of each leaflet, a special, white, toothlike structure, packed with fats and proteins, offers food to the ants, which are thus provided with both room and board. So peculiar is this relationship that it has even been given a name: myrmecophily, or love for ants in plants.

"Genetic" galls develop without the aid of external stimulus. They arise entirely as a result of this tobacco plant's internal make-up. Controlled by the genes, this tumor condition is hereditary in nature.

The advantages of these structures for ants are obvious, but it is not so clear how the plants profit from them. Since many of these myrmecophilous plants were first found in areas infested by leaf-cutting ants, it was suggested that perhaps defense was the answer—that the plants attracted one harmless species of ant in order to keep another harmful species away. But this turned out not to be the case, for during an invasion by leaf-cutting ants, the boarder ants scurried for cover. As an alternate possibility I suggest that boarder ants leave droppings and debris in their hosts, which use this material as food to help them survive in areas of low nutrient supply.

Crown galls, stimulated by bacteria, most often appear on plant surfaces that are cut or injured. The bacterium induces excessive production of a plant hormone which in turn promotes the growth of the galls.

Oᴎᴇ of the oddest relationships between plants and animals occurs in galls, the remarkable malformations, often as large as ping-pong balls, which develop on leaves or branches when certain gall insects lay their eggs in them. When a gall wasp, for instance, saws off the tip of an oak bud and lays its eggs on the cut surface, the oak cells will start to grow around the eggs, ultimately producing a very complex structure, entirely unlike any other part of the tree.

The stimulus for this unusual growth is apparently provided by the larva, which secretes growth substances which make the plant cells grow out of all proportion. Each species of gall insect, furthermore, induces the growth of a different structure, so it would seem that each must produce a different set of growth substances. When one type of larva is full grown, it has to tunnel its way out of the gall to pupate near the surface. In certain other galls, however, the outer tissues are too hard for the larva to break through; in this case, the gall forms a plug which drops out at the proper time, setting the larva free. There are even galls which have a fungus growing inside, left there by the parent insect when it lays its eggs—in this case, the larva feeds on the fungus.

Many an innocent reader may look in a book on plants for an exciting account of the man-eating tree of Madagascar or other similar terrifying plants. Actually, the biggest animal I ever saw trapped by a plant was a cockroach, drowned in a pitcher plant—an experience apparently equally traumatic to the pitcher, for it had died too. The fact is that there are no plants which attack larger animals, and if man or animal does become entangled in plants in the jungle, it is not by design of the plant but by carelessness of the intruder.

One of the early classics in the story of carnivorous or insectivorous plants was published by Charles Darwin. He noted that sundew plants, which have sticky tentacles on their tiny leaves, caught tiny insects, much as flypaper catches flies, holding them while neighboring tentacles bent over to pin the victims against the leaf, where their bodies were decomposed by enzymes. Darwin found that any tiny piece of meat or egg white was handled by the sundew leaf in the same way it digested insects.

THERE are many other plants which have developed insectivorous habits. Most of them, like the sundew, are found in nutrient-poor bogs. *Pinguicula* is very similar to sundew but less complex: it too traps insects with its sticky leaf glands and then rolls the edge of a leaf over its victims. The strange, urn-shaped leaves of pitcher plants standing with some watery liquid in their base are a common sight from North Carolina to Florida and Mississippi. Inside are usually found a few insects such as ants and moths, caught because of a lining of downward-pointing hairs which prevent them from crawling out of the pitcher. Bacteria and enzymes in the water decompose and digest them.

An even more elaborate trapping mechanism is found in a group of tropical Asiatic lianas, the *Nepenthes*, whose beautifully sculptured pitchers hang on long leaf stalks which are twisted around tree branches for support. Insects are first attracted by a distinctive odor; then, near the entrance of the trap, they find nectar-secreting glands. To reach these, they have to scale the leaf rim, which usually results in their falling into the pitcher and a pool of mildly digestive fluid at the bottom. If they try to crawl out, they first have to pass a region with digestive glands, then a highly polished slippery zone. Most of them never get beyond this; if they do, they face an overhang at the rim with a spiked edge.

One of the best known of insectivorous plants is the Venus's-flytrap (*Dionaea*) of North Carolina, a relative of the sundew but with an entirely different way of catching prey. The leaves lie in a rosette flat on the ground and each ends in a leaf blade which looks and acts like a steel trap. The two halves of the leaf, about the size of a nickel, are hinged in the middle. When an insect walks on its surface, the leaf will suddenly snap closed, the toothed edges meshing. The Venus's-flytrap can distinguish between a living and a dead object—small sticks or pebbles will leave it undisturbed—by means of three sensitive hairs on each leaf half. The leaf will not close unless two hairs are touched in succession or the same hair twice. Once shut, the trap gradually pinches tighter and tighter, squeezing its prey against the digestive glands on the leaf surface.

The prize for complexity in trapping devices unquestionably goes to the bladderwort, *Utricularia*, a water plant with beautiful blue or yellow flowers, found in ponds and ditches. On its submerged threadlike stems it has innumerable bladders in which tiny water creatures get caught. At one end of the bladder is a trap door which suddenly snaps open when sensory hairs just outside the trap are touched. The tiny victim is sucked in so fast that it cannot be followed by the eye or the movie camera. The door then closes, part of the water is pumped out from the inside, and the trap is set for another catch.

THICK SKIN AND ABUNDANT SPINES REDUCE WATER LOSS AND DISCOURAGE ANIMALS FROM EATING GOLDEN BARREL AND OLD-MAN CACTI

Partners and Parasites

Although most plants are considered independent because they make their food by means of photosynthesis, many are actually dependent on their relationships with other living forms—both plant and animal—for a successful life. These associations may range from the casual and seemingly haphazard to ties that are so close that the death of one partner means the doom of the other.

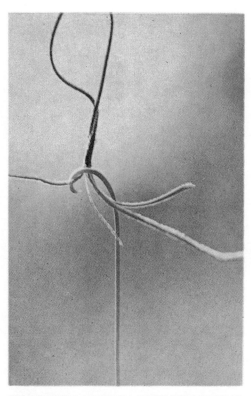

SPANISH MOSS ANCHORS A GREEN SMILAX TENDRIL

LADY-IN-THE-NIGHT, an epiphytic orchid, anchors itself on trees with cells that grow from under its roots into cracks in the bark. Spongy, white root tissue absorbs and stores water.

WRAPPED AROUND AN OAK, the horizontal roots of a 16-year-old liana support its thick stem seen at right. This liana also has vertical roots that reach to the ground and nourish it.

A Reach to the Sun

To reach the light that they need to sustain life in the shady forests, lianas and epiphytes, each in their special way, depend on sturdier plants such as trees for their support. Hoisting themselves from the ground in which they are rooted, lianas may twine, creep or hook their way up the trees that serve them as scaffolds, assisted variously by tendrils, thorns or sucker roots.

Most familiar lianas of the Temperate Zone, such as honeysuckles and ivies, have thin stems. But in the moist tropics most favorable to their lush growth, other species have stems as thick as arms. They are not parasites, but get their food and water from the soil, and their supple woody stems have conducting tubes adapted to their enormous lengths—up to 650 feet in some climbing rattans. Once lianas pierce the sunlit forest roof, they bear leaves and flowers. These are usually invisible from the shadowed forest floor, where only a knotted tangle of stems hints at the active life high above.

lIANAS LOOP a 75-foot sweetgum in a Florida forest. As they meander in typical fashion between the tree and the ground, their sinuous stems create a virtually impenetrable tangle.

WATER IN QUANTITY is absorbed by leaves of this bromeliad along their entire length. They stock up when it rains, storing water in fleshy bases to survive dry spells.

Strange Lives on Platforms

The particular problem of epiphytes, which have sacrificed all connections to the ground in their efforts to reach sunlight, is securing nutrients and water. With no roots in the soil, they have had to develop unusual mechanisms to hang on to every crumb of humus and drop of moisture. Some of these are shown here—the thick-skinned and succulent leaves that retain water for the bromeliad at the left, and the network of aerial roots that extend from the arum below at the right. Some of these plants, such as the epiphytic arums, may dangle their roots down as far as 60 feet to pull up water from a stream below. Less dramatic but more familiar epiphytes include a number of lichens, mosses, liverworts, ferns, and even a few cacti.

DECAYING MATTER piles up on the horizontal limbs of a kapok, building fertile soil for epiphytes, which grow in every nook and cranny but not on the smooth trunk.

HUMUS IN CREVICES of bark holds food and water for rare "blue" orchids in the Amazon basin. Their roots hold them on this lofty perch and also absorb nutrients.

ROOTS IN THE AIR sustain an arum high in the rain forest. Their large surface area in proportion to plant size helps them drink quickly from any passing shower.

A SPROUTING DODDER stretches its tendril-like stem *(left above)* toward a green host plant only 12 hours after emerging from its seed. A day later *(center)* the dodder stem has coiled itself firmly around its victim. A week later *(right)*, after developing rootlike organs that invade the host, the dodder breaks its ties with the ground and becomes a full-fledged parasite.

Deadly Dependents

Plants that have little or no chlorophyll—about a tenth of all the world's species—cannot manufacture their own food and must get it in some other way. One method is that used by the saprophytes, mostly bacteria and fungi that feed on dead or decaying organisms or on dead parts of plants living nearby. The Indian pipe, one of the few flowering saprophytes, obtains all of its organic food and minerals by means of a mutually beneficial association with fungi growing underground. These surround its roots and supply it with the nutrients from digested forest litter.

In contrast to these scavengers are the many parasitic plants that feed only on living organisms, deriving all or most of their food and water from green plants. Dodder, for example, with no true leaves or roots, winds sinuous threads around its host to supply itself with food. The deadly dodder, however, also has enemies of its own—at least two kinds of aphids afflict it, extending the chain of eat and be eaten from the plant to the animal kingdom.

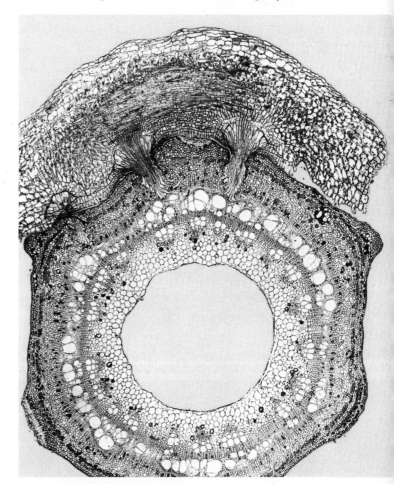

TRANSLUCENT INDIAN PIPES thrive among decayed leaves. Common in the Temperate Zone, they survive best in shade. They cannot photosynthesize, since they have no chlorophyll.

ROOTLIKE PROCESSES of the dodder, known as haustoria, are seen through a microscope, invading a plant stalk. With these, the dodder taps the host's conducting vessels for nutrients.

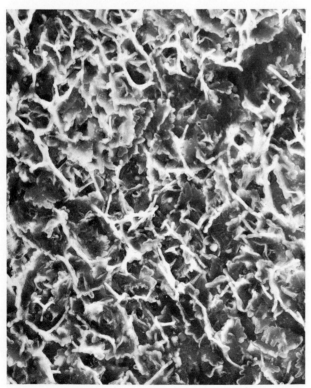

The Meat Eaters

A few plants turn the tables on the animal kingdom by eating animals themselves. The devices that trap live prey range in size from the microscopic snares grown by some fungi to pitchers with a capacity of seven pints of liquid, which grow in Borneo. Usually found in nitrogen-poor bogs, insectivorous plants can survive without prey, but apparently their victims provide a nitrogen supplement to the nutrients these plants obtain in the usual manner.

Most of the traps used by plant carnivores are formed from modified leaves. These tend to follow three basic models. One resembles a steel trap and clamps the halves of its leaves shut over its victims. Another, like flypaper, snarls its prey in sticky secretions. The third is the pitcher, shown here, which lures insects to a watery death at its base. Less well known are the fungi which trap tiny soil-dwelling nematode worms, using gluey knobs on the ends of short stalks, or specialized three-celled nooses. Because nematodes cause crop damage exceeding one billion dollars a year, the use of such fungi by man to control these pests is being carefully studied.

TAPERING PITCHERS of the trumpet plant entice insects to enter with nectar that coats their rims. Inside, stiff, downward curving hairs and slippery walls effectively foil escape.

WAXY WALL, lining a pitcher interior between its rim and the fluid below, is seen with an electron microscope. The wall is double, with a wax base topped by a layer of irregular scales.

SLIPPERY SCALES like these found on the feet of a trapped fly show why it loses its foothold. As more and more wax particles stick to the fly's feet, it can only slide down to its doom.

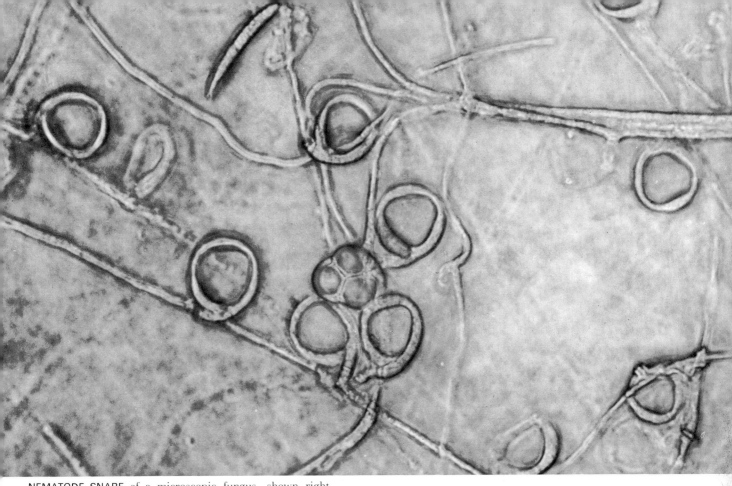

NEMATODE SNARE of a microscopic fungus, shown right above two open loops in the center of this photograph, swells shut at a touch. Gaping open, others await any passing prey.

FATALLY TRAPPED, the nematode shown below is secured by three snares each only a thousandth of an inch thick. Death will be quick as the prey is invaded by fungus filaments.

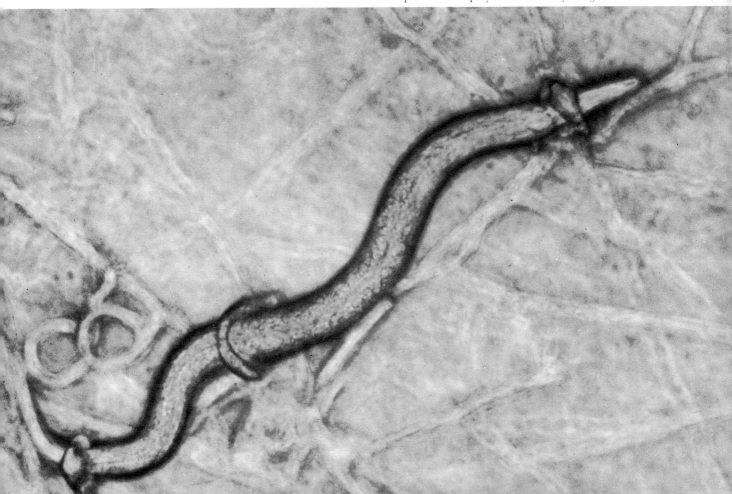

Living Shelters

Plant galls may be caused by the action of such widely different agents as bacteria, fungi and viruses, but the most elaborate and uniform galls are those induced by insects. Insect galls are round, egg-shaped, spindle-shaped, or even look like thin disks or ropy mosses. Their outer shells may be smooth or sticky, hairy or bumpy. In spite of this astonishing variety, gall insects are highly specific in selecting their plant hosts. A scant 12 plant families—among them roses, goldenrods, willows and oaks—harbor almost three quarters of the 2,000 insect galls that are known in North America. The gall wasps alone account for more than 800 of these unusual structures, and oak trees are the most favored targets. Wasps can induce 275 different sorts of galls on the leaves of oaks, 175 sorts on oak stems, 45 on buds, 41 on roots and 55 others on their acorns and flowers.

Galls supply the developing insect larvae with both food and shelter, so that insects obviously gain by their gall-making propensity. The plant, however, does not benefit and, if it loses large amounts of its own food materials, may even be harmed.

ROUND SWELLINGS on the stems of goldenrod are mature galls stimulated by eggs of the gallfly, deposited two months before. These galls appear at the same height on every plant.

A SNUG SHELTER for a gallfly larva is revealed when the goldenrod gall is opened. Outside, the gall is hard and smooth. Inside it is filled with spongy tissue on which the larva feeds.

A TINY TUNNEL dug by the larva is the mature fly's path to freedom. The sac on its head, which pumps air in and out like a bellows, is strong enough to crack the gall's tough shell.

156

8

Man
the
Master

ALTHOUGH man is certainly a product of nature, classified as a mammal, he clearly can no longer be considered a part of nature. With his tools, his chemicals, his means of transportation and especially his powers of reason and research, he has long since become a force apart from nature. This is particularly true of man's relationship to plants: his role has to be considered separately from that of any other influence in their environment. The central fact of this role is that man is today capable of controlling plants—he has, in effect, become a new force where plants are concerned.

Is this good or bad for man and the plant world? The question is really irrelevant, for this development was inevitable. As long as man gathered food, collecting the fruits of the forest and the seeds and roots of the field, he did not differ from ant or squirrel as a part of nature, and his numbers were limited accordingly. Food for the gatherer is not very abundant—in any type of vegetation there are only relatively few plants which provide nourishment, the others being poisonous, bitter, astringent, low in food value or indigestible. Thus the so-called carrying capacity of natural vegetation for man was and still is very low. The most primitive natives of today, who live entirely on natural vegetation and animals, are not much better off than the gorillas or orangutans of the jungle, of which there are only several thousand alive. Restricted largely to eating fruits, leaves and the shoots of very young trees, the numbers of these anthropoid apes have declined steadily for millennia, as have the numbers of our most primitive human tribes.

On this basis we can make an estimate of the maximum number of people who inhabited the earth before man started to manage nature by cultivating certain plants he liked as food. In all the world, they may not have counted more than about three million, and probably were fewer than that. The Australian aborigines are of all people still closest to primitive man, with no agriculture, and there are about 40,000 of them living today under semicivilized conditions. In North America, we know that about 150,000 Plains Indians were able to subsist in a game-rich area of perhaps 600,000 square miles, living as nomads, hunting, gathering roots and berries, rarely growing small crops. In South America today, native Indians require a hunting area of well over 10 square miles per human, probably comparable to what primitive man required. Figuring an inhabitable earth surface of about 30 million square miles in very early times, this all points to the same low natural carrying capacity of the earth for man.

Considering these figures, it is obvious what agriculture really means to man. With a present world population of more than three billion people, we are living a thousandfold beyond what a balanced nature could allow, what natural food resources would make possible. In other words, if man were to have to revert to nature, only one person out of every 1,000 alive today would be able to survive.

THE development of agriculture, therefore, was one of man's truly great advances, comparable to his taming of fire. The cultivation of plants which provided food, fibers and other products not only enabled him to lead a more abundant life, but also freed him from the natural limitations of his environment, making it possible for him to increase his numbers far beyond those of any of the other higher animals. Whereas hunting with the club and the spear was only an extension of what carnivorous animals had done since the beginnings of creation, agriculture was an entirely new endeavor, the control of nature to provide man with his food needs.

How and when did agriculture begin? This is a question we can only speculate on—the earliest beginnings are lost in the dawn of history. We know that from the time of the first settled humans, from neolithic man in Asia Minor and Europe to the early Indians in America, agriculture grew from pulling weeds to aid the growth of wild grain and other useful plants to deliberately sowing crops and finally plowing the soil. But just where the first seed was sown and what manner of man—or woman—sowed it, we shall never know.

Most likely, the beginnings were gradual. A particularly vigorous plant may have developed in some grove or meadow favored by a primitive tribe, and its seeds may not all have been eaten, but some planted for the following season. In some of the oldest Indian campsites two-inch corncobs have been unearthed; more recent campsites, indicating a progressive cultivation, have yielded four-inch cobs. It is not at all illogical to suppose that primitive man, seeing that some plants grew more abundantly than others, would attempt to favor the more fruitful varieties. It is also possible that larger and better varieties of plants were obtained now and again by barter or trade between neighboring

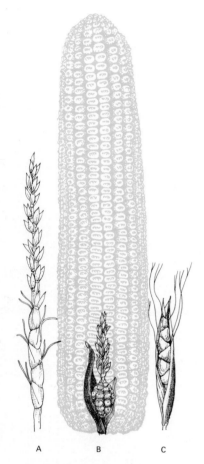

A   B   C

THE ANCESTRY OF CORN

Wild corn was first domesticated at least 7,000 years ago by the Indians of tropical America, who then crossbred corn plants from various American areas. Later, they bred corn with Tripsacum (A), a wild grass relative, producing teosinte (C), a cornlike grass. Teosinte, in turn, was crossbred with true corn, and stronger, larger varieties resulted. Further selective breeding improved these hybrids, and the success of these efforts is symbolized by the dent corn (color) above. Its yield of 500 to 1,000 kernels per cob contrasts with that of the earliest known cultivated corn (B)—only 48 kernels.

tribes, thus allowing the superior plants to spread over increasingly larger areas.

What really taxes the imagination is how primitive man, with no scientific knowledge at all, developed all the major food-crop plants to such a remarkable degree of perfection. It is astonishing to contemplate that today, with all our detailed information about selection and heredity, and our powerful scientific methods, we have added only one major new food crop to the list of corn, wheat, rye, barley, oats, millet, rice, beans, peas, soybeans, squash and all the other staples which man has known for countless generations. That one new crop is the sugar beet, developed within the last two centuries for primarily economic reasons, to make the regions of the temperate world less dependent on the tropical sugar cane.

Sowing seeds for crops, of course, was only part of the story, the very beginning of it. Agricultural methods had to be devised to aid the propagation of the growing plant. New varieties of plants had to be developed which would germinate readily when sown and which would produce sufficient amounts of food and other useful products under the growing conditions of the environment. There was an urgency to this, for when man began to cultivate plants, he also was able to settle down, and as his food supplies increased, his numbers increased too and he became more and more dependent on what he could take from the soil.

The most primitive method of agriculture doubtless was to drop seeds in small clearings, giving the seedling a chance to grow before the natural vegetation closed in again. This type of agriculture was used by the natives of Sumatra and Borneo in relatively modern times when they started their rubber tree plantings. The next stage was the preparation of a larger cleared area, a little field tilled by hoeing or otherwise turning over the soil. In Peru this is still done with a wooden planting peg. Then came protection of the seedling plants against the encroachment of native vegetation—weeding the fields. Next, perhaps, followed the sowing of several different plants together which might help each other, as, for instance, corn plants whose stalks would serve as supports for beans. A still further step was the use of the plow and ultimately the harnessing of animals to pull it, making possible the cultivation of increasingly larger areas.

Irrigation was another innovation already achieved in prehistoric times. Present-day Indians still sow corn in river beds immediately after spring floods have drenched the soil, indicating how the idea of irrigation may have originated. The Nabataeans, pre-Christian traders and agriculturists of Palestine, carried it further, building simple dams to break the force of flash floods and spread their waters over valley floors, a system which pointed the way to the modern methods of bringing extra water to the soil before planting.

And now, as man settled, cities grew and brought with them an entirely new agricultural problem—exhaustion of the soil. In such favored lands as Egypt, yearly floods brought ever-new supplies of nutrients to replenish those used up by intensive cultivation, but elsewhere, as in the Tigris and Euphrates valley, excessive irrigation led to silting of the land and salting of the irrigation water —the same thing that is happening today in California and in the Rio Grande valley on the border between Texas and Mexico. Great civilizations fell when the soil gave out. And even in areas with a plentiful water supply, manuring became essential, but it was still not enough to support the natural growth of populations, and so nations began to reach out across their borders and even across the seas to obtain the food and other plant staples which they required.

With mass cultivation, new problems of erosion, weed, pest and disease control, soil conservation and maintenance of fertility have arisen. Erosion is one of the most serious, occurring wherever unprotected soil lies open to strong winds or excessive rainfall. Since about 40 per cent of our cultivated plants, covering more than 80 per cent of our croplands, are annuals which have to be resown each year on bare soil, the problem of protecting these fields in autumn, winter and spring has assumed major importance. The loss of topsoil is only one of erosion's harmful effects; it also causes leaching of nutrients from the soil, particularly serious in tropical countries with high rainfall. This forces the agricultural populations to clear new areas regularly for their primitive cultivation, abandoning the leached soil of their fields to further erosion and destroying more and more primeval forest.

T HE advent of agriculture also brought with it the new concept of a weed. Any plant can be a weed; it depends entirely on where it grows and how man is involved. Basically, a weed is an unintended plant, growing where we do not want it. A tomato in our flower garden is a weed; a zinnia would be a weed in a tomato field. (Without human help tomatoes do not grow anywhere except in their native country, Peru, the only place where they find the correct natural conditions for germination and growth.) Most weeds today have a worldwide distribution, brought about by man. Before the sailing vessel, steamship, railroad and airplane, the spread of plants was slow and limited. But now a shipment of grain from Canada can bring a New World weed into England, and during the last 100 years we have seen the invasion of Europe by American weeds such as *Galinsoga*, and of America by European weeds such as the Russian thistle, the Klamath weed and many others, all of which, if unchecked, can seriously affect the productivity of cultivated crops.

The most important of all the new factors which in modern times have revo-

FIVE MAN-MADE PLANT MIGRATIONS

BREADFRUIT: *Discovered in Polynesia in 1688 by the English adventurer William Dampier, this tropical plant was the goal of Captain Bligh's famed voyage a century later. The tree was brought to the New World to feed slave labor.*

POTATO: *Whether the Spaniards or the English first brought the potato from the New World as a foodstuff is in dispute. In any case, the nutritious crop became so popular that emigrants from Ireland introduced it to North America in 1719.*

PINEAPPLE: *No one knows how this New World plant traveled from tropical America to Hawaii. But a favorable climate and assiduous care have produced a fruit so delicious that Hawaii now produces one third of the world's yearly crop.*

COFFEE: *As raw berry or roasted bean, coffee has served as a stimulant for over 10 centuries—at first in its native Africa and then spreading to Asia and the New World. Today's main cash coffee crops are raised in South and Central America.*

RUBBER: *Native to the Amazon Basin, rubber was a Brazilian monopoly until 1875. That year, the British smuggled the seeds of 7,000 rubber trees out of Brazil, hidden in pots which contained innocent specimens of rare tropical plants.*

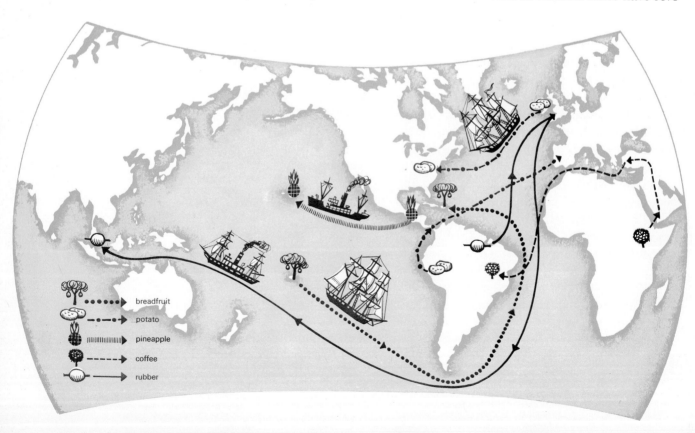

breadfruit
potato
pineapple
coffee
rubber

lutionized agriculture is research. Even the development of machinery, enabling a single farmer to cultivate an area which less than 100 years ago would have required a labor force of 10 men and 20 horses, has not wrought as significant a change in man's present abilities and future prospects as has the work of the botanist and the agricultural scientist. Through all the ages, plant cultivation was a matter of knowledge developed by trial and error and handed down from father to son; now research has made it possible for man to ask intelligent questions of nature and to receive the answers, through experiments, unequivocally from nature itself. Research has led to fundamental advances that are crucial to the survival of man on his increasingly crowded planet.

The first and most important discovery of research was that intensive cropping removes part of the "working capital" of nutrients from the soil. As simple as this principle may seem to us today, its recognition over a century ago was an agricultural milestone. It led in 1840 to Liebig's formulation of "the law of the minimum," which says that crop yield is limited by the minimum amount of any one of the essential mineral nutrients in the soil—and this is the whole basis of the modern concept of fertilizer application.

Another giant step about a century ago was the discovery that plant diseases may be caused by pathogenic organisms which have invaded a crop plant. In human terms, this was equivalent to Koch's and Pasteur's discovery of the role of microbes in human disease: it enabled the farmer to prevent plant diseases. No farmer can treat individual plants affected by disease; the task is too immense, and their lack of a circulatory system makes application of curative drugs far more difficult than in animals. But preventing disease is a thoroughly practical matter—one can spray with fungicides, for example, or with chemicals designed to cut short the life cycle of a disease-bearing organism—and the results in terms of stable harvests and increased productivity can be little short of phenomenal. Although the late blight of potatoes is still an ever-present menace, a calamity like that which befell Ireland is as unlikely today in any agriculturally up-to-date nation as an epidemic of Black Death.

Research has also given us the laws of heredity and the control of genes, two developments whose impact has been felt around the world. They made possible the extensive and purposeful breeding of new varieties of plants with higher yields and greater resistance to unfavorable climates and disease. The ability to chemically double the chromosomes in plants opened vast new possibilities for hybridization (the breeding of hybrid corn alone increased corn yields by more than 25 per cent), and artificial mutation with high-energy radiation or chemical treatment furnishes the plant breeder with additional tools for developing new varieties.

SIMILARLY, the study of the ancestry of crop plants and the discovery through taxonomic research of close relationships contributed both to disease prevention and increased crop yields. A wild grass in Israel, for example, which showed important qualities of resistance to wheat rust, was found to be related to domestic wheat, making it possible to transmit its rust-resistant qualities to the cultivated plant—another step in controlling this most insidious disease.

A richly rewarding field of research over the last 50 years has been that of mineral nutrition and the function of trace elements. Without minute amounts of these trace elements, no plant can develop normally. Thus mottled leaves in orange and other fruit trees were proved to be due to lack of traces of zinc in the soil; likewise, injured growing points in cauliflowers may be caused by insufficient boron. These discoveries led to speedy diagnosis of trace-element deficiencies in other plants. One find leads to another, and now the development of chelated iron and other metal compounds has made possible the treatment of many cases of yellowness, or lack of chlorophyll, in crop species.

The study of photoperiodism, the response of a growing plant to the length of day, has given scientists possibilities of controlling or influencing plant growth unthought of a half century ago. Plant hormones, less than 40 years ago entirely unknown, have opened the way to improve the rooting of cuttings, or the development of seedless fruits and many other things. Spraying with plant hormones can prevent premature fruit drop in apples, induce flowering in pineapples (where it is desirable) and prevent it in sugar cane (where it is not). Organic weed killers, first developed some 20 years ago, are chemically related to plant hormones but, because of a slight modification in their chemical structure, are toxic instead of beneficial. This opens an entirely new and selective way of controlling weeds.

Still in its infancy is the study of the effects of climatic factors on plants in air-conditioned laboratories. Here again, however, research has already shown the value of fundamental knowledge when applied to the growing conditions of plants in nature and in fields—knowledge which leads to more effective control of cultivated plants.

RESEARCH, as is now generally recognized, is a short cut to solving almost any problem, and in plants, which are slow-growing at best by the impatient standards of man, this has a particular value. Today plant research is carried out in laboratories all over the world, but a century ago the situation was quite different. Much of our early plant information came from European universities where professors of botany carried out such fundamental research as they were able to in addition to their heavy teaching duties. Then, with the passage of the Morrill Act in 1862, the United States pioneered in providing government funds for agricultural research, with the result that scientists were specifically employed to study crop plants.

This example has been followed all over the world and now the agricultural experiment station is a fundamental tool for the improvement of agriculture in almost every country. In underdeveloped lands it provides one of the brightest hopes for improved national development. Many of the large plantation industries, such as sugar cane, rubber, pineapple, tobacco and coffee, have their own experiment stations, and some of the biggest individual growers have private research departments, but most of the research on crop plants is carried out by the government-sponsored institutions.

Universities and private institutions still contribute their share to research, particularly to the increase of fundamental knowledge of plants. Organizations like the Boyce Thompson Institute for Plant Research, the California Institute of Technology, Harvard University and the University of Chicago have very significantly advanced our knowledge of the fundamentals of botany. Similarly, work carried out in private botanical gardens, such as the Arnold Arboretum near Boston and the Missouri Botanical Garden, is advancing knowledge about garden plants.

The area open to research in the plant world seems almost inexhaustible and the possibilities may well be thought limitless. Of all the hundreds of thousands of plants in existence, only a few thousand have so far been used by man. Once it becomes established that a plant has economic value, botanists start investigating, breeding, selecting and improving it. Its closest relatives in the wilds are collected and hybridized to introduce other, more desirable characteristics into the cultivated plant, such as rust resistance in wheat or temperature tolerance in tomatoes and peas.

This last emphasizes the importance which wild plants will always have in the further development of useful cultivated species. If the wild vegetation is destroyed to make room for man's needs, we will have lost a priceless reservoir for future crop improvements, for we will be unable to draw upon the almost infinite variability and ingenuity which nature has produced during millions of years of evolution. For this reason alone we should jealously preserve large tracts of land in their original state as repositories of the riches of nature, for we will never be able to replace them once they are destroyed. And we certainly cannot predict which plants might become economically important during the next thousands of years. Once our fossil fuels, coal and oil, have been consumed we will depend for energy and raw products more upon the sun and upon plants than ever before, even with atomic energy available.

Such conservation of original, unspoiled nature is particularly difficult in primitive countries, where the expanding native population still depends so much on the natural resources of forests and fields. There, enormous amounts of wild, potentially valuable vegetation have been destroyed. In Borneo, for instance, most of the lowland forest was eradicated to make way for primitive and very wasteful rubber plantings. Orchids, which are certainly valuable for things other than corsages (vanilla, for example, is an orchid), have been decimated all over the world by collectors of these spectacular flowers—many species of *Cattleya* in South America and *Phalaenopsis* in Indonesia and Malaya have become so rare that they soon may not exist anywhere in the wild.

It is, of course, impossible to mention here the approximately 1,000 different kinds of plants which are grown commercially for food, fibers, beverages, drugs, oils, resins, tannins, cork, lumber, rubber and dozens of other special needs. Among the most important to man are those used as animal food—the hay, alfalfa, clover and other fodders grown in pastures to feed livestock, and the corn and oats which also go into meat production. We in our meat-rich Western civilization seldom stop to consider that on the average only about 10 per cent of the energy in the plant products fed to cows, hogs and chickens can actually be harvested as meat; but to many of the underdeveloped countries living on the verge of famine this is a vital factor. They cannot waste that much energy; to them meat is a luxury which can be ill afforded.

THIS matter of the amount of energy that can be harvested from a food chain is of urgent importance to man's future. In general there is a 90 per cent loss at each link of a food chain when animal eats animal or plant. The loss is particularly appalling in the sea. Tuna and other large fish feed on smaller fish; these smaller ones feed on creatures of the plankton, mainly crustaceans; and these in turn feed on algae. When we eat tuna, therefore, what with the general heat-energy loss in the sea, we are reaping in food value less than one five-hundred thousandth of the original light energy which fell upon the algae in the sea. This is one reason why, in spite of the high primary productivity of sea water in terms of algae (at least near shore and in shallow waters), the ocean is not likely to become the major source of human food.

Considering this, what does all the new knowledge in botany mean to man? Simply this: while medicine has made possible the alarming increase in world population, plant research so far has enabled man to stay ahead, though barely, of the specter of starvation. This critical balance between two undoubted assets of modern life highlights the quandary of our times. What are the prospects that the explosively increasing population of the world can be sustained by a further increase in food production?

At present only 10 per cent of the earth's land surface is used for crop production, with another 19 per cent used as meadows and pastures, most of which indirectly produces meat. If necessary, part of this latter could be used for crop production. Part of the 30 per cent now covered with forests could go into cultivation too, and if the population pressure is great enough, more desert and other wasteland could be made arable by irrigation, drainage and fertilization. All in all, we could say optimistically that, if necessary, we could increase the area of arable land fourfold.

A second factor in food production is the yield per acre. In the United States this is higher on the average than in most other countries because of more intensive cultivation and greater use of fertilizers. Even so, our corn yield averages but 54 bushels per acre, a figure which with all-out efforts could be increased more than threefold. Taking the world as a whole, and disregarding the question of economy, it can be said that over-all food production per acre, too, could be multiplied about four times.

A FURTHER gain in available food calories could be obtained by a change-over from animal to predominantly plant food. This applies particularly to the United States, New Zealand and other meat-rich countries, but it would not affect India, Japan, China or the Southeast Asian countries, where animal food supplies less than five per cent of all the food calories.

Adding all this together, we could, by applying our present agricultural know-how, increase present world food production about 20 times. This is a hopeful figure but a rather dismal prospect. It would mean no space left for recreation or for living, a meatless diet for meat lovers, enormous increases in fertilizer factories and equally enormous increases in the cost of food.

There is another prospect for increasing food production, one which lies in heightened efficiency of food production *by the plant*. Under natural conditions, plants convert only slightly more than two per cent of the sun's light energy into chemical energy, and only half of this can be used as food. Theoretically, however, a plant could convert 10 per cent of the light energy, a fivefold increase of its present maximum light utilization. Whether anywhere near this fivefold increase could actually be achieved is questionable, but some increase is not beyond the realm of possibility. Research scientists will have to create entirely new methods to improve the efficiency of light utilization by plants, and this would only be possible if we achieve a deeper understanding of photosynthesis and plant growth.

All these estimates of increased production, of course, assume that we will have complete control of pests and diseases which even today still wreak havoc in agricultural production. This is a large assumption, for mass cultivation definitely leads to intensified attacks of disease and pests. This has been proved time and again in rubber plantations: whereas the widely spaced native rubber trees in the jungle are not particularly affected by local leaf blight, any plantation in the area may be decimated by it. The same thing happens with insect attacks: single plants are generally not badly infected, but when grown in large numbers they fall prey to aphids, caterpillars and other insect predators. Nor are the natural enemies of these insects of much avail under conditions of mass cultivation—once the crop has been harvested, they can survive only if they find a continuing food supply. This is why man has turned to chemical control of pests and diseases; and just as surely as man cannot survive without advanced agriculture, agriculture cannot survive without the judicious application of insecticides, fungicides and herbicides.

It is not the purpose of this book to enter the argument about the use of these poisons which has been given such wide prominence by Rachel Carson's *Silent Spring*. Miss Carson, in denouncing the indiscriminate use of poison sprays, is generally quite correct: any poison must be used with care. However, man has reached the point where he cannot exist without them. We live on the brink of starvation, almost at the mercy of insects, diseases and weeds. Only the United States and a few other technologically advanced countries have been able to achieve a measure of control over these problems and dangers. The careful and selective use of the modern insecticides, fungicides and herbicides is the only way this control can be maintained and broadened to other parts of the world. The bitter lesson is that we must learn to live with poisons, if we are to live at all.

Let us now draw up a balance of debits and credits as regards man's management of plants and the future of the earth. We have seen how very intricately human life is tied up with plants. All the energy necessary to maintain life in the animal and human body is garnered by plants from light energy captured in the photosynthetic reduction of carbon dioxide. Since the biochemistry of the animal or human cell is so very much like that of the plant cell, the food stored by plants is immediately usable by the body of man—something that is not true for any other kind of energy, whether nuclear, wind, water, electrical or derived from heat. But plants profit from man as well. Daily our botanists, agriculturists, horticulturists, foresters, plant pathologists, entomologists, soil scientists, plant breeders and dozens of other specialists contribute to the improvement of plants, and farmers work long hours to make crops thrive.

Optimists point out that where man has managed wisely in his best agricultural areas, the productivity of the soil has improved with no indications of exhaustion, because man is distributing the mineral nutrients more evenly. He is mining potassium and phosphorus where they were uselessly concentrated in mineral deposits and is spreading them evenly on agricultural soils where they do the most good. He has planted parks and gardens, relieving the monotony of the original vegetation. Through exploration and breeding he has created high-yield food plants delicious to the taste, and his successes in breeding superbly beautiful flowers are phenomenal.

ON the other side of the ledger, we must admit that man has often needlessly destroyed appalling numbers of forests and other types of vegetation without providing for regrowth; he has caused terrible water and wind erosion through unwise use of land; he is losing and in the near future will have lost through extinction thousands of plant species which evolution had created over hundreds of millions of years and which never can be replaced. To repeat, no one can say what plants might become vitally important in the agriculture or forestry of the future. We simply *must* heed the warnings and the proposals of conservationists; we *must* act before these species have become extinct, before erosion and fire and deforestation have taken a greater toll of our vegetation and soils.

As we have seen, plants can sense and respond to light, gravity and many other stimuli in their environment. But since they have no nervous system, they cannot feel the way animals do: they are emotionless. No message of pain can be sent to a central brain or to a center of feeling. It is therefore also certain that plants cannot have a mind and cannot possibly be held accountable for their actions: every movement or reaction of a plant is inevitably bound by the narrow limits of its hormonal response mechanism, with no latitude for voluntary decisions. And yet, despite this fact, I believe that observation of plants can teach all of us certain moral lessons.

Nature as a whole, comprising both plants and animals, is often termed cruel, because of the merciless struggle for existence in which no quarter is asked for or given. This fierce competition is often used as an apology for war, since mutual extermination would seem to be nature's way of keeping populations in proportion. But consider now what happens in the plant world.

Remarkably enough, plants have few weapons or defense mechanisms with which they attack or fend off other plants. This does not mean that they have to submit to any parasite which comes near them: all have more or less effective structures or reactions capable of preventing fungus or bacterium from penetrating and attacking them. It is usually the plants struggling under poor growing conditions in places where they should not be which are attacked most by pests and diseases; plants in favorable circumstances are much less beset by insects and parasitic fungi.

But what are the relations between individual plants in a forest or other type of vegetation? Do they struggle with each other? Do they fight for a place in the sun? What are the decisive factors determining which one of the thousands of acorns or chestnuts produced by a single tree will ultimately replace it when it dies? Is there the same awful attrition of seedlings and young trees as there is of tadpoles or young salmon, of which many thousands hatch, but only a scant few grow up to mature?

S EEKING a case of extreme competition between individual plants, I thought I had found it in the desert. When, on rare occasions, a heavy rain awakens the seeds which have been lying dormant in the desert sands during the dry years, a thousand or more seedlings may sprout on every square foot of this usually barren soil. They may be so dense that the seedling leaves cover the surface with a carpet of green. Everything I had ever read about evolution prepared me to find at such a time a jockeying for supremacy, a struggle for space and an ultimate victory of a few plants which managed to outgrow the others. And what actually happened?

All of these seedlings grew. They grew slowly, to be sure, but more than half of them got far enough in that arid habitat to form a few leaves, at least one flower and ultimately a few seeds. It was *not* a case of a few outgrowing the others and monopolizing the light, moisture and nutrients—they grew up evenly, equally sharing available space. It was clear that if a seed of a desert annual plant once manages to germinate, it has a better than even chance to grow up into a mature plant and to fulfill its function or mission of producing at least one but usually more seeds. There is no violent struggle between plants, no warlike mutual killing, but a harmonious development on a share-and-share-alike basis. The cooperative principle is stronger than the competitive one: the controlling factor in the desert's carpet of flowers is the germination of the seed, and it is differential germination which regulates the plant population in the world. In other words, not war, but birth control is nature's answer.

LIKE SOME MONSTROUS LABYRINTH, IRRIGATED SUGAR CANE FIELDS DOMINATE THE FERTILE LOWLANDS OF MAUI IN THE HAWAIIAN ISLANDS

A Race against Hunger

Committed for over 200,000 years to the life of wandering, man settled down for the first time 10,000 years ago when he learned to satisfy his hunger by growing most of his food. The domestication of wild plants created a new life of abundance. But now we face a problem—how to make the productivity of the soil match mankind's rocketing numbers by establishing a new balance of nature.

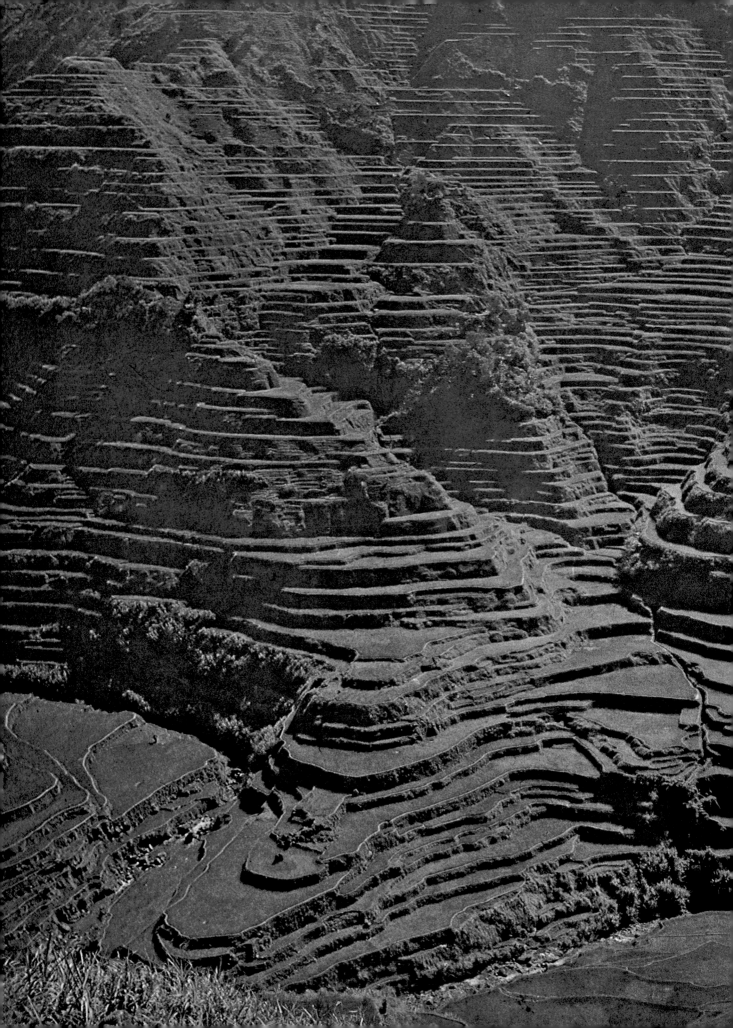

A Revolution Built on Seeds of Grass

The dawn of civilization is inextricably entwined with the shadowy, prehistoric beginnings of agriculture. For until men learned how to grow their own food, they were forced to live an essentially nomadic existence, driven by hunger from exhausted to fresh hunting grounds. The first great change in this harsh and thinly peopled way of life took place about 10,000 years ago, somewhere within the borders of the Middle East. Here men had long gathered the edible seeds of two wild grasses that grew in the hills. Now they purposely planted these prized seeds and raised the grains that became the ancestors of modern wheat and barley.

This agricultural revolution reoccurred elsewhere, always with similar results —the founding of communities and an upsurge of human energies. It is no coincidence that such key elements of civilization as writing, metallurgy and growth of towns and cities followed in its wake.

LIKE FLIGHTS OF STAIRS, terraced rice fields rise to the very tops of these Philippine hills. Rice, another of the grasses that became staple grains, may well have been the first crop raised in the Far East.

The Substance of the Old World

The six different kinds of seeds in the still life above constitute some of mankind's oldest and most basic foods. Kernels of wheat cover the stone hand mill; barley and oats flood the wooden bowls; and dried peas, unpolished rice and red lentils of the type used by Jacob to make a "red pottage" for hungry Esau fill the baskets. Spread into a sunburst behind these loose seeds is a sheaf of ripe wheat, the grain that continues to occupy the top place among the

world's cereals. Wheat is grown on nearly one third of the land devoted to grain production, and more tons of wheat are harvested annually than of rice, although rice has the higher yield per seed planted and remains the chief staple for more of humanity. Before a taste for leavened bread among the ancients led to an increase in wheat production, easily grown barley had an importance similar to rice's today and was the hearty fare of peasants and soldiers.

172

The Bounty of the New World

Gold was not the only valuable commodity seized from the Americas by the conquistadors. There were foods of kinds never before seen by white men and so delicious and nutritious as to revolutionize the eating habits of Europe and eventually of the world. Shown above are some of the staples that the Indians had produced from wild stock and brought to a high degree of perfection in pre-Columbian times. Maize, for example, had been grown by man in New World gardens for so long that it had completely lost the ability to reproduce itself.

Transported from American to European soil, these new foods flourished. White and sweet potatoes, plump squash and protein-rich beans proved a boon to the poor. And maize filled barns and larders as they had rarely been filled before—returning an average of 250 kernels for each kernel planted, tenfold the yield from any of the Old World grains.

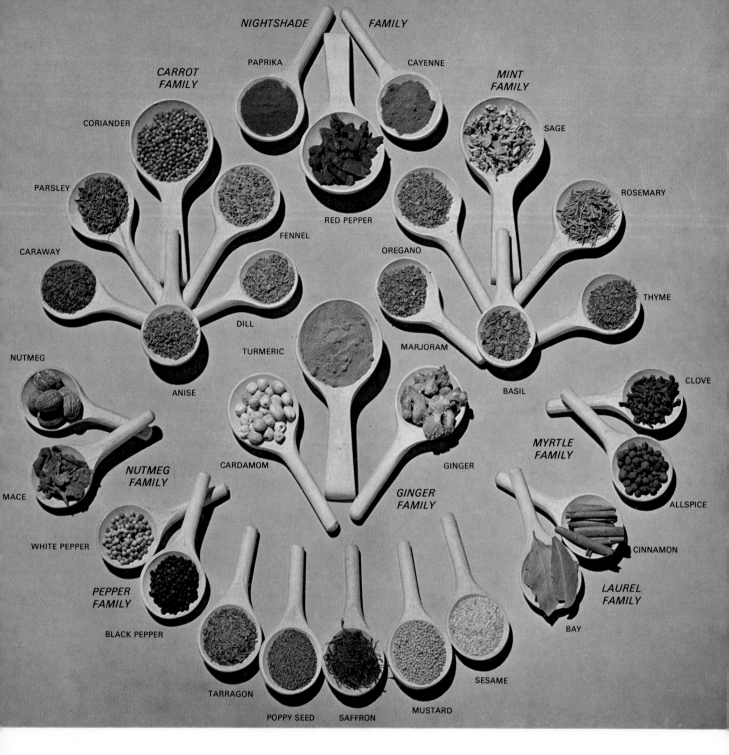

NIGHTSHADE FAMILY

PAPRIKA CAYENNE

CARROT FAMILY

MINT FAMILY

CORIANDER SAGE

PARSLEY RED PEPPER ROSEMARY

FENNEL

CARAWAY OREGANO THYME

DILL

NUTMEG TURMERIC MARJORAM CLOVE

ANISE BASIL

MACE CARDAMOM GINGER MYRTLE FAMILY

NUTMEG FAMILY GINGER FAMILY ALLSPICE

WHITE PEPPER CINNAMON

PEPPER FAMILY LAUREL FAMILY

BLACK PEPPER BAY

SESAME

TARRAGON MUSTARD

POPPY SEED SAFFRON

A Taste for the Finer Things

The inner bark of an evergreen, the unopened flower buds of a tree, the rhizome of a herbaceous perennial, the stigmas and styles of a late-blooming bulb—all are highly prized as flavorings for food. These spices are better known as cinnamon, cloves, ginger and saffron. All four are included in the photograph above, along with 27 other commonly used herbs and spices consisting of dried leaves, roots, seeds, berries and fruits. Grouped together to indicate their relationship to each other, they represent 13 different families in the plant kingdom. Though most are now cultivated over a fairly extensive range, many, such as rosemary, tarragon, dill, anise and bay, came originally from the Mediterranean area. Others, like basil, black pepper, nutmeg, mace and cloves, came from the Orient, for many years the focus of the spice trade, in its heyday an enormously lucrative business—and still a very lively one.

An Abundant, Man-made Harvest

A hunger for plant foods has led man to experiment with many edible wild varieties from which, late or soon, have come the vegetables we consume today. The appetizing display of greens and roots shown above demonstrates man's selective influence on a single family—the mustards. Green and red cabbages, cauliflowers, broccoli, Brussels sprouts, rutabagas, kohlrabies and turnips are all believed to have been developed from a single mustard an-

cestor, a wild cabbage. Green cabbage was eaten during the Bronze Age and was popular among the Egyptians and Romans, who also had an appetite for such other tangy mustards as watercress, horseradish and radishes. Red cabbage and kohlrabi, on the other hand, were not known until the Middle Ages, and broccoli and cauliflower not until the 16th Century. Brussels sprouts are newcomers indeed, developed as recently as the early 1800s.

175

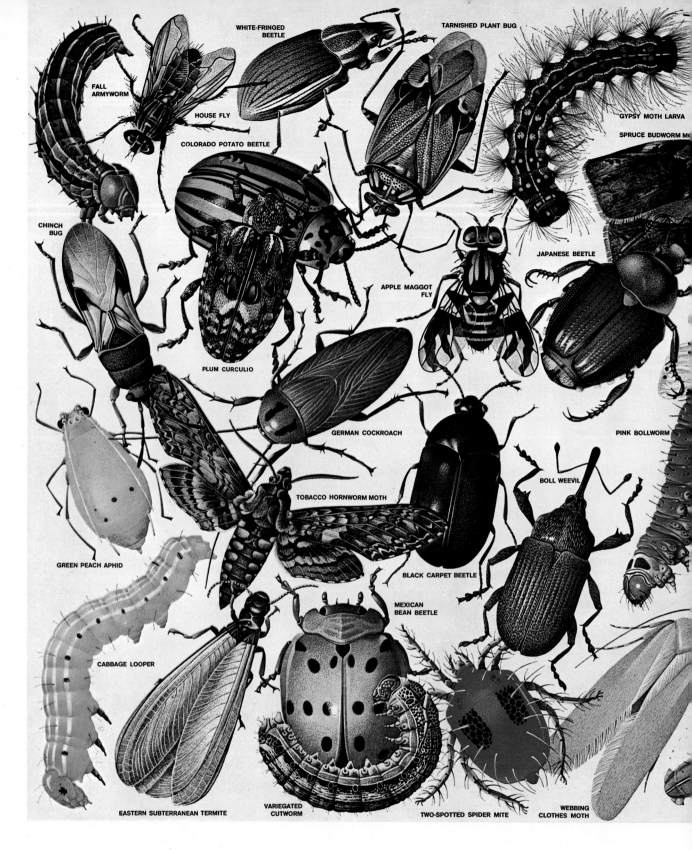

FALL ARMYWORM

WHITE-FRINGED BEETLE

TARNISHED PLANT BUG

HOUSE FLY

COLORADO POTATO BEETLE

GYPSY MOTH LARVA

SPRUCE BUDWORM M

CHINCH BUG

JAPANESE BEETLE

APPLE MAGGOT FLY

PLUM CURCULIO

GERMAN COCKROACH

PINK BOLLWORM

BOLL WEEVIL

TOBACCO HORNWORM MOTH

GREEN PEACH APHID

BLACK CARPET BEETLE

MEXICAN BEAN BEETLE

CABBAGE LOOPER

EASTERN SUBTERRANEAN TERMITE

VARIEGATED CUTWORM

TWO-SPOTTED SPIDER MITE

WEBBING CLOTHES MOTH

A Host of Active Enemies

Many of the plants that man depends upon most for his livelihood are prey to insect pests. Forty-eight of the worst offenders in the United States are depicted above. As a destroyer, the boll weevil leads the field. Although $75 million is spent each year trying to control it, the weevil causes $225 million

176

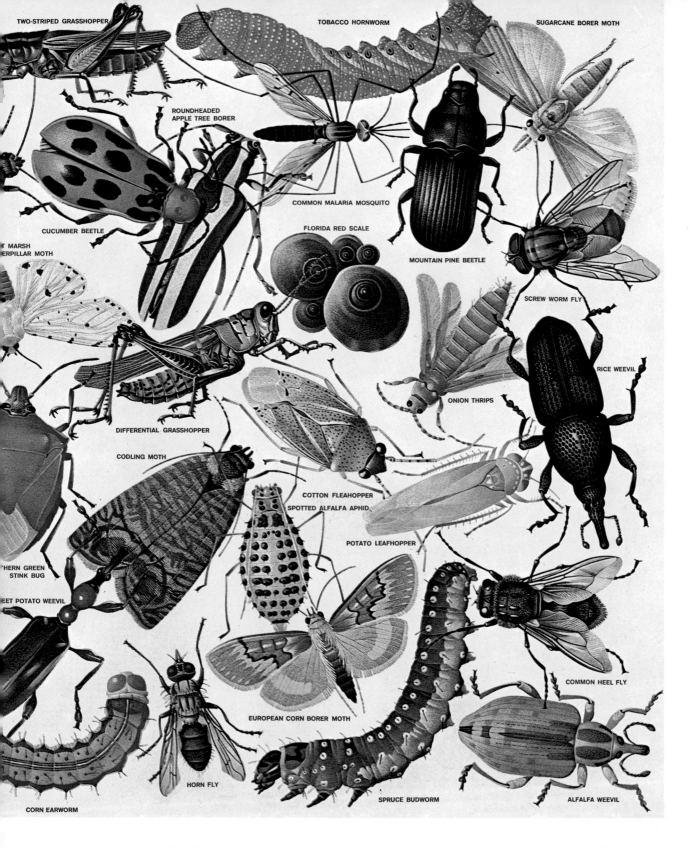

TWO-STRIPED GRASSHOPPER

TOBACCO HORNWORM

SUGARCANE BORER MOTH

ROUNDHEADED
APPLE TREE BORER

COMMON MALARIA MOSQUITO

CUCUMBER BEETLE

FLORIDA RED SCALE

MOUNTAIN PINE BEETLE

MARSH
ERPILLAR MOTH

SCREW WORM FLY

RICE WEEVIL

DIFFERENTIAL GRASSHOPPER

ONION THRIPS

CODLING MOTH

COTTON FLEAHOPPER
SPOTTED ALFALFA APHID

POTATO LEAFHOPPER

HERN GREEN
STINK BUG

EET POTATO WEEVIL

COMMON HEEL FLY

EUROPEAN CORN BORER MOTH

HORN FLY

SPRUCE BUDWORM

ALFALFA WEEVIL

CORN EARWORM

worth of damage annually. Forests suffer from the spruce budworm, gypsy moth and mountain pine beetle. The last alone causes a yearly timber loss of $10 million. The codling moth, if left unchecked, would cut United States apple production by at least half. A number of pests, such as the Japanese beetle, the gypsy moth, the alfalfa weevil and the European corn borer, came from abroad. Once here, with none of their native diseases and enemies to keep them in check, such insects proliferated unbelievably. All told, the cost of insect pest control in the United States comes to approximately $655 million a year.

A VORACIOUS FEEDER, the spotted alfalfa aphid can be controlled with the aid of natural enemies, as this painting based on a California study shows. The aphids are being attacked in three ways: by wasps, which lay their eggs inside them; by big-eyed bugs, adult and larval lady beetles and green lacewings, which eat them; and by a fungus disease *(center stalk)*.

BY KILLING THE TOBACCO HORNWORM FOR FOOD, POLISTES, OR PAPER WASPS, HAVE WON A WELCOME FOR THEMSELVES IN TOBACCO FIELDS

The Helpful Balance of Nature

In seeking ways to control insect pests, scientists have turned to insect predators for help. They have had outstanding success in several instances, and if the predators themselves pose no threats as potential pests, such natural methods of control can be widely applied. A classic case of the use of insect against insect is shown opposite. Among the species employed to destroy the spotted alfalfa aphid is the *Trioxys* wasp, imported to California from the Near East; it is depicted laying eggs in an aphid on the second stalk from the left. Another case of natural control is the use of *Polistes*, the familiar paper wasps, in tobacco fields. The wasps tidily butcher tobacco hornworms and carry the meat away to feed the home brood. Thus they offer an attractive alternative to chemical poisons which, unless carefully applied, can leave a residue that affects the flavor of the tobacco.

Insects have also been recruited to fight another group of agricultural pests—the weeds. One weed-feeding beetle, brought to America from Europe in the 1940s, is eating the West clean of a plant menace—the Klamath weed—itself imported accidentally from Europe. And the cinnabar moth, introduced recently from France, has made inroads on yet another European immigrant, the tansy ragwort.

A War for Survival

With 30 per cent of the world's population undernourished, scientists are hard pressed to find new ways of increasing food production. Even more people would be hungry today except for the advances agricultural science has already achieved. It has vastly improved the environment for crops through the development of fertilizers, insecticides and weed killers—so much so that present levels of food production would fall disastrously if these were not used. Science also has cut the incidence of disease among plants through the breeding of strains that resist infection. Botanists have crossed different varieties of the same plant to produce hybrids with multiplied yields and they have tailored plants to specific climates and various growing conditions.

A list of these accomplishments would be nearly endless, but the question arises whether even widespread adaptation of some or all of these advances by underdeveloped nations will be enough to stave off hunger. Only 15 years from now, the world's population is expected to have risen from three billion to four billion and the numbers of the undernourished will have grown proportionately. And further increases in the world's food supply, by themselves, cannot solve the problem posed by the even greater population rise expected in the more distant future.

RESEARCH is indispensable in the fight against hunger, and even the purest of "pure research" can produce useful results. Here, apricot seedlings are being tested in a wind tunnel to determine the effect of various wind velocities on their growth.

APPLICATION of research discoveries makes possible the use of new weapons against pests, such as the aerial spraying seen here. Not only are insecticides, weed killers and fertilizers applied in this way, but crops are sown and made ready for harvest.

THE PLANT KINGDOM

This brief guide traces the march of evolution that has seen plants develop from primitive water dwellers to today's 250,000 flowering herbs, shrubs and trees. Such a guide, of course, can only hint at the variety of the plant kingdom, with its total of some 375,000 living species.

The plants are divided into two subkingdoms, thallophytes and embryophytes. All the former are absolutely dependent on a water environment for reproduction. These simpler plants range in size from microscopic bacteria to giant seaweeds. The algae and a few bacteria contain chlorophyll, but the fungi and most bacteria do not.

The embryophytes have grown increasingly independent of a water environment for reproduction. Mostly land dwellers, they have developed roots, stems and leaves, and a vascular system that distributes water throughout the plant. The production of seeds and the development of flowers are these plants' most recent evolutionary advances.

I. SUBKINGDOM THALLOPHYTA

A. DIVISION SCHIZOPHYTA

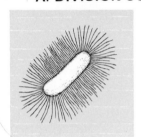

i. CLASS SCHIZOMYCETES

The bacteria are tiny one-celled organisms, some probably similar to the earliest forms of life. They flourish in almost every environment. Some promote decay, making nutrients available to the higher plants. Some cause diseases, others are of economic importance. Illustrated: *Escherichia*

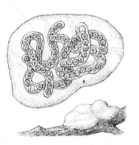

ii. CLASS CYANOPHYCEAE

The blue-green algae are the simplest of the plants that contain chlorophyll-*a*. They also contain pigments that give them a blue to reddish color. Many keep soils fertile by fixing atmospheric nitrogen. Some species can even live in hot springs. Illustrated: *Nostoc*

B. DIVISION RHODOPHYTA

i. CLASS BANGIOPHYCEAE

These primitive red algae often resemble certain blue-green algae in color. Some show a complex branched structure. Most are marine plants, attached to rocks in the intertidal zone. A few live in water as deep as 600 feet, using the dim blue light there for photosynthesis. Illustrated: *Porphyra*

ii. CLASS FLORIDEOPHYCEAE

Most of the advanced red algae are found in tropical and semi-tropical seas, but there are also fresh-water and temperate-ocean species. One of them, Irish moss, produces carrageenin, an emulsifier and stabilizer. Others are cultivated as food, primarily in Japan. Illustrated: *Polysiphonia*

C. DIVISION CHLOROPHYTA

i. CLASS CHLOROPHYCEAE

The green algae, ancestral to the embryophytes, occur in salt and fresh water and also in moist land environments. They are a basic food source for aquatic animals. Some grow as single cells, some as filaments or leafy forms and some even resemble higher plants. Illustrated: *Spirogyra*

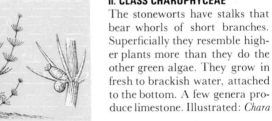

ii. CLASS CHAROPHYCEAE

The stoneworts have stalks that bear whorls of short branches. Superficially they resemble higher plants more than they do the other green algae. They grow in fresh to brackish water, attached to the bottom. A few genera produce limestone. Illustrated: *Chara*

D. DIVISION EUGLENOPHYTA

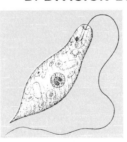

CLASS EUGLENOPHYCEAE

The euglenoids, one-celled, free-swimming flagellated algae, have characteristics of both plants and animals. They have been claimed by both botanists and zoologists. Because these plants have evolved in the direction of the protozoa, they are important in evolutionary study. Illustrated: *Euglena*

E. DIVISION PYRROPHYTA

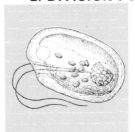

i. CLASS CRYPTOPHYCEAE

Most cryptophytes are one-celled aquatic plants. There are few genera in this class and they have not been studied extensively. Most possess a prominent gullet and are very animal-like. Some cryptophytes may have been ancestral to the flagellated protozoa. Illustrated: *Cryptomonas*

DIVISION PYRROPHYTA *continued*

G. DIVISION PHAEOPHYTA

ii. CLASS DESMOPHYCEAE

The desmophytes are another group of primarily one-celled marine algae of tropical waters. They include only half a dozen genera and have not been extensively studied as to habitat or classification. They are closely related to the class below—the dinoflagellates'. Illustrated: *Exuviaella*

i. CLASS ISOGENERATAE

These marine brown algae, the most primitive in their division, are ancestral to the two classes that follow. They have a flattened, many-branched stalk and typically are anchored by a holdfast. Some are used as fertilizer; others are burned to recover potassium and iodine. Illustrated: *Dictyota*

iii. CLASS DINOPHYCEAE

The microscopic ocean-dwelling dinoflagellates form an important part of the plankton—the basic food source for marine animals. They are primarily responsible for the phosphorescence of tropical seas. Some species cause the "red tide," coloring the seas and killing fish. Illustrated: *Peridinium*

ii. CLASS HETEROGENERATAE

This class of marine brown algae includes the familiar kelps. Usually anchored by holdfasts, they show a narrow leaflike structure. Kelps are used as food in Japan. One giant species of the Pacific coast may grow to several hundred feet, making it the world's longest plant. Illustrated: *Laminaria*

F. DIVISION CHRYSOPHYTA

i. CLASS CHLOROMONADOPHYCEAE

The free-swimming chloromonads are one-celled green or yellow-green algae that may form temporary colonies. A small class with very few genera, the chloromonads are of little importance aside from the fact that, like all marine algae, they contribute to the ocean food chain. Illustrated: *Gonyostomum*

iii. CLASS CYCLOSPORAE

These seaweeds are the most advanced and specialized of the brown algae. Like the kelps, they have a flat, ribbonlike structure, but typically they possess rows of tiny air bladders along their fronds. The free-floating sargassum weed of the subtropical Atlantic is of this class. Illustrated: *Fucus*

ii. CLASS XANTHOPHYCEAE

The yellow-green algae are found in fresh water or wet soil, growing singly or in colonies. Some soil-growing species possess rootlike filaments. Neither common nor abundant, this class is nonetheless of considerable interest from an evolutionary viewpoint. Illustrated: *Vaucheria*

H. DIVISION FUNGI

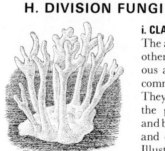

i. CLASS MYXOMYCETES

The affinity of the slime molds to other fungi is obscure. Inconspicuous amoebalike plants, they are common in dead vegetable matter. They flow slowly along or through the ground, engulfing bacteria and bits of organic matter as food and depositing a trail of slime. Illustrated: *Cerateomyxa*

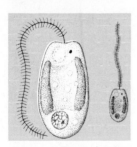

iii. CLASS CHRYSOPHYCEAE

The golden algae, one-celled or colonial, are usually found in fresh water. Some inhabit swift streams in branched colonies three feet long. Marine species form a part —but, except for the abundant silicoflagellates, not an important part—of the ocean's food chain. Illustrated: *Chromulina*

ii. CLASS PHYCOMYCETES

These fungi include the water molds, some mildews and the common bread mold. They usually grow in filaments, called hyphae, and have definite cell walls. They may be parasites of plants and animals. One phycomycete blight caused the potato famine in Ireland. Illustrated: *Rhizopus*

iv. CLASS BACILLARIOPHYCEAE

The diatoms, the largest class of algae, are also the most abundant single form of plankton. Their cell walls, impregnated with silica, have fossilized in vast numbers. Called diatomaceous earth, these fossils are mined for use as filter and binder material. Illustrated: *Actinoptychus (left), Triceratium*

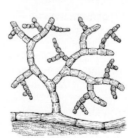

iii. CLASS ASCOMYCETES

These fungi include the yeasts, the powdery mildews and pink bread mold. A fungus of this class caused the chestnut blight in the United States. But many of these fungi are useful to man—yeasts that cause fermentation, and the molds that synthesize antibiotics. Illustrated: *Neurospora*

iv. CLASS BASIDIOMYCETES
The most familiar members of this class are the mushrooms, with their distinctive fruiting bodies. Also included are rusts and smuts that cause great agricultural losses. The basidiomycetes, like all fungi, are major agents of decay. Illustrated: *Cantharellus*

II. SUBKINGDOM EMBRYOPHYTA

A. DIVISION BRYOPHYTA

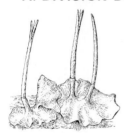

i. CLASS ANTHOCEROTAE
The horned liverworts are among the most primitive of living embryophytes. They differ from the true liverworts in possessing a rudimentary gas exchange system, with openings located on the lower surface of their leaflike fronds. Illustrated: *Anthoceros*

ii. CLASS HEPATICAE
Liverworts, whose ancestors must have been among the earliest of land plants, are chiefly tropical. Although they have leaflike and stemlike structures, they do not possess true roots, stems or leaves, or specialized conducting tissues as do the more advanced plants. Illustrated: *Marchantia*

iii. CLASS MUSCI
The mosses, found especially in moist habitats, grow everywhere from the tropics to arctic regions. Many take foothold on bare surfaces and initiate the process of soil building. The peat mosses have long been used as fuel. Illustrated: *Polytrichium*

B. DIVISION PSILOPHYTA

CLASS PSILOTAE
Psilophytes are the most primitive of the plants that possess specialized conducting tissues, and the other vascular plants probably are derived from them. They have branched green stems and rhizomes but do not have true roots. Illustrated: *Psilotum*

C. DIVISION LEPIDOPHYTA

CLASS LYCOPODIAE
The club mosses and quillworts have developed true roots as well as branched stems and tiny narrow leaves. They are remnants of a once more abundant class. Lepidodendrons, extinct members of this group, are among the fossil plants of today's coal beds. Illustrated: *Selaginella*

D. DIVISION CALAMOPHYTA

CLASS EQUISETAE
Horsetails are also remnants of a once abundant group. Marsh plants with jointed stems that end in conelike tips, they are found throughout the world except Australia. The calamites, extinct relatives, flourished in the Mesozoic. Illustrated: *Equisetum*

E. DIVISION FILICOPHYTA

CLASS FILICES
Ferns, the largest group of vascular plants that do not form seeds, were a dominant flora in the early Mesozoic era. Today, their 10,000 species—some of them tree-sized—grow in a variety of climates but favor moist shady regions. Illustrated: *Pteridium*

F. DIVISION CYCADOPHYTA

CLASS CYCADAE
The living cycads are also remnants of a once larger group. Fernlike, with large compound leaves, they bear seeds in a terminal cone. This and the next division are called gymnosperms, or "naked seeds": their seeds are not in an ovary. Illustrated: *Zamia*

G. DIVISION CONIFEROPHYTA

i. CLASS CONIFERAE
These are primarily cone-bearing trees—pine, fir, spruce, cedar—but include the yew and ginkgo. Conifers dominate the forests of the colder Temperate Zone. They are of economic importance as sources of lumber and wood pulp for paper, as well as resins and turpentine. Illustrated: *Pinus*

ii. CLASS CHLAMYDOSPERMAE
Although grouped with the conifers, this small class is of debatable affinity and may represent an evolutionary dead end. Of its three genera, *Gnetum* is a tropical woody vine or shrub, *Ephedra* is a desert shrub, and *Welwitschia* is found only in Southwest Africa. Illustrated: *Ephedra*

H. DIVISION ANTHOPHYTA

The flowering plants, or angiosperms, are the most familiar of all botanical groups, outnumbering the rest of the plant kingdom. All 10 orders of the smaller, more advanced class, the monocots, are listed here, but only the 24 more abundant of the 47 orders of dicots have been selected for inclusion.

WEEPING WILLOW

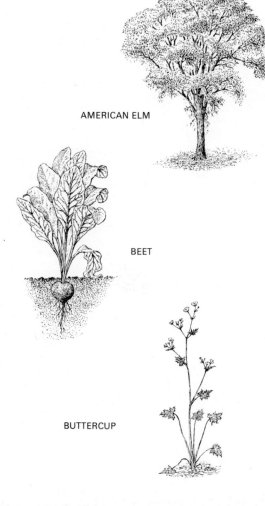

AMERICAN ELM

BEET

BUTTERCUP

DIVISION ANTHOPHYTA *continued*

i. CLASS DICOTYLEDONEAE

Order Piperales: Herbaceous, mainly tropical—only three families. Seeds of one species—*Piper nigrum*—provide black (unripe) and white (ripe) pepper.

Order Salicales: Trees and shrubs, temperate to arctic—only one family. An economically important order, it includes poplar, willow, aspen and cottonwood.

Order Myricales: Trees and shrubs, temperate to subtropical—only one family. The waxy fruit of one species, the bayberry, is used to make scented candles.

Order Juglandales: Temperate Zone trees—only one family. Three genera, walnut, pecan and hickory, bear edible nuts. Walnut is valued as a decorative wood.

Order Fagales: Trees, temperate to subtropical—only two families, birch and beech. Chestnut and oak, valuable hardwoods, are both of the beech family.

Order Urticales: Trees and shrubs, mainly tropical—four families. American elm and mulberry are temperate members; banyan and breadfruit tropical.

Order Polygonales: Mainly temperate herbs and shrubs—only one family. Familiar are buckwheat—the only important dicot food grain—and rhubarb.

Order Centrospermae: Herbs, shrubs, some trees, temperate to tropical—10 large families. Familiar species include beet, spinach, carnation, four-o'clock.

Order Ranales: Herbs through trees, worldwide range—19 families. Little-modified descendants of primitive anthophytes, they include magnolia and buttercup.

Order Rhoeadales: Mostly herbs and shrubs, subtropical to temperate—seven families. One, the mustard family, includes 11 familiar vegetables (*see p. 175*).

Order Sarraceniales: Herbaceous, temperate to tropical—only three families. The order includes the insectivorous pitchers, sundew and Venus's-flytrap.

Order Rosales: Herbs through trees, worldwide distribution—17 important families. Here are found many fruits, the legumes (including wisteria), sycamore.

Order Geraniales: Herbs through trees, temperate to tropical—21 families; over 5,000 species. Familiar members include citrus, mahogany, rubber, myrrh.

Order Sapindales: Mainly Temperate Zone shrubs and trees—23 families. The order includes maple, horse chestnut, holly, pistachio, sumac, poison ivy.

Order Rhamnales: Shrubs and trees, tropical to temperate—only two families. The grapes include Virginia creeper; the buckthorns include cascara and jujube.

Order Parietales: Herbs and trees, tropical to temperate—the largest order; 31 families. Its varied members run from tea to papaya, from violet to begonia.

Order Opuntiales: Herbaceous or woody, tropical to temperate—only one family. New World natives, the cacti extend from Argentina north to Canada.

Order Myrtiflorae: Herbs and trees, worldwide range—23 families. Economically important members include pomegranate, allspice, clove, eucalyptus.

WISTERIA

ORANGE

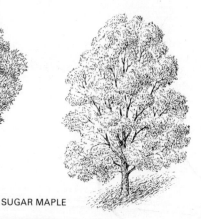

SUGAR MAPLE

Order Umbelliflorae: Herbs through trees, tropical to temperate—only three families. One large family, the carrot, includes celery, parsley, fennel and dill.

Order Ericales: Herbs through trees, tropical to cold temperate —four families. One, the heaths, includes blueberry, cranberry, rhododendron, azalea, heather.

Order Tubiflorae: Herbs to trees, tropics to cold temperate— 23 families. One includes potato, tomato and tobacco; another, the mints; a third, sweet potato.

Order Rubiales: Herbs through trees, tropical to temperate—five families. The largest of these (5,000 species) includes coffee, quinine, ipecac and the gardenia.

Order Cucurbitales: Herbaceous, initially subtropical to tropical—only one family. It contains the pumpkin, squash, cucumber, citron and all melons.

Order Campanulatae: Herbs through trees, tropical to arctic— six families. The 20,000 species of composites are the most advanced dicots. Example: sunflower.

CUCUMBER

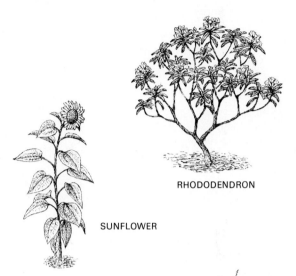

RHODODENDRON

SUNFLOWER

ii. CLASS MONOCOTYLEDONEAE

Order Pandanales: Herbs, a few trees, tropical to arctic—only three families. Two are marsh plants—cattail and bur reed. The third is the tropical screwpine.

Order Helobiae: Herbaceous, worldwide—seven families. All are marsh or water plants. Many species are eaten by waterfowl and provide shelter for fishes.

Order Glumiflorae: Herbaceous, worldwide—two families (grasses and sedges). The most economically valuable of all monocots are the cereal grasses.

Order Principes: Vines through trees, tropical to subtropical— only one family (4,000 species). This order includes rattan and all true palms—coconut and the like.

Order Synanthae: Herbaceous, tropical—only one family. The name "Panama-hat palm" describes its use. It stands between the true palms and the arums.

Order Spathiflorae: Herbaceous, tropical to temperate— only two families. One, the arums (1,500 species), includes jack-in-the-pulpit and the philodendron.

Order Farinosae: Herbaceous, tropical to temperate—13 families. One, the bromeliads (2,000 species), includes the pineapple, the caroá fiber and Spanish moss.

Order Liliiflorae: Herbaceous, worldwide—eight families. One, the lilies (4,000 species), dominates this order. It includes many flowers, the onion and asparagus.

Order Scitamineae: Herbaceous, tropical to subtropical— four families. A highly advanced order, it includes the banana, ginger and arrowroot.

Order Microspermae: Herbaceous, worldwide—two families. One, the orchids, is the most advanced and reproductively specialized in the plant kingdom.

MAIZE

COCONUT

ONION

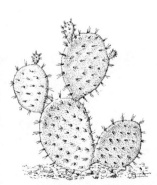

PRICKLY PEAR CACTUS

CATTLEYA ORCHID

187

Bibliography

General

Bailey, L. H., *Manual of Cultivated Plants* (rev. ed.). Macmillan, 1949.

Cronquist, Arthur, *Introductory Botany*. Harper & Row, 1961.

Fuller, Harry J., and Oswald Tippo, *College Botany* (rev. ed.). Holt, Rinehart & Winston, 1954.

Greulach, Victor A., and J. Edison Adams, *Plants, An Introduction to Modern Botany*. John Wiley & Sons, 1962.

Hill, Albert F., *Economic Botany* (2nd ed.). McGraw-Hill, 1952.

Hill, J. Ben, Lee O. Overholts, Henry W. Popp and Alvin R. Grove Jr., *Botany* (3rd ed.). McGraw-Hill, 1960.

Jaeger, Paul, *The Wonderful Life of Flowers*. E. P. Dutton, 1961.

†Moment, Gairdner B., ed., *Frontiers of Modern Biology*. Houghton Mifflin, 1962.

†Ray, Peter Martin, *The Living Plant*. Holt, Rinehart & Winston, 1963.

Reed, Howard S., *A Short History of the Plant Sciences*. Chronica Botanica, 1942.

Robbins, Wilfred William, T. E. Weier and Ralph Stocking, *Botany, An Introduction to Plant Science* (2nd ed.). John Wiley & Sons, 1957.

Sinnott, Edmund W. and Katherine S. Wilson, *Botany* (6th ed.). McGraw-Hill, 1963.

†Sistrom, W. R., *Microbial Life*. Holt, Rinehart & Winston, 1962.

Transeau, E. N., H. C. Sampson and L. H. Tiffany, *Textbook of Botany* (rev. ed.). Harper & Row, 1953.

Wilson, Carl L. and Walter E. Loomis, *Botany* (3rd rev. ed.). Holt, Rinehart & Winston, 1962.

Evolution and Classification

Andrews, Henry N. Jr., *Studies in Paleobotany*. John Wiley & Sons, 1961.

Arnold, Chester A., *An Introduction to Paleobotany*. McGraw-Hill, 1947.

Benson, Lyman, *Plant Classification*. D. C. Heath, 1956.

*Bold, Harold C., *The Plant Kingdom*. Prentice-Hall, 1960.

Delevoryas, Theodore, *Morphology and Evolution of Fossil Plants*. Holt, Rinehart & Winston, 1962.

Gleason, Henry A., *The New Britton and Brown Illustrated Flora* (3 vols.). New York Botanical Garden, 1952.

Gray, Asa and Merritt Lyndon Fernald, *Manual of Botany* (8th ed.). American Book, 1950.

Hellyer, A.G.L., *The Encyclopaedia of Plant Portraits*. Transatlantic Arts, 1953.

Lawrence, George H. M., *Taxonomy of Vascular Plants*. Macmillan, 1951.

Pool, Raymond J., *Flowers and Flowering Plants* (2nd ed.). McGraw-Hill, 1941.

Seward, A. C., *Plant Life through the Ages* (2nd ed.). Hafner, 1959.

Anatomy and Physiology

Bold, Harold C., *Morphology of Plants*. Harper & Row, 1957.

Bonner, James and Arthur W. Galston, *Principles of Plant Physiology*. W. H. Freeman, 1952.

Dodd, John D., *Form and Function in Plants*. Iowa State University Press, 1962.

Esau, Katherine, *Anatomy of Seed Plants*. John Wiley & Sons, 1960. *Plant Anatomy*. John Wiley & Sons, 1953.

†Fogg, G. E., *The Growth of Plants*. Penguin Books, 1963.

*Galston, Arthur W., *The Life of the Green Plant*. Prentice-Hall, 1961.

*Gerard, R. W., *Unresting Cells*. Harper Torchbook, 1949.

Haupt, Arthur W., *Plant Morphology*. McGraw-Hill, 1953.

Hillman, W. S., *The Physiology of Flowering*. Holt, Rinehart & Winston, 1962.

†Lee, Addison E. and Charles Heimsch, *Development and Structure of Plants*. Holt, Rinehart & Winston, 1962.

Meyer, Bernard S., Donald B. Anderson and Richard H. Bohning, *Introduction to Plant Physiology*. Van Nostrand, 1960.

Steward, F. C., ed., *Plant Physiology*, (Vols. IA and IB). Academic Press, 1960.

Strafford, G. A., *Plant Metabolism*. Harvard University Press, 1963.

*Swanson, Carl P., *The Cell*. Prentice-Hall, 1960.

Went, Frits W., *The Experimental Control of Plant Growth*. Ronald, 1957.

Wolken, Jerome J., *Euglena*. Rutgers University Press, 1961.

Specific Plants

Clair, Colin, *Of Herbs and Spices*. Abelard-Schuman, 1961.

Cobb, Boughton, *A Field Guide to the Ferns*. Houghton Mifflin, 1956.

Harrison, S. G., *Garden Shrubs and Trees*. St. Martin's Press, 1960.

Howes, Paul Griswold, *The Giant Cactus Forest and Its World*. Duell, Sloan & Pearce, 1954.

†Large, E. C., *The Advance of the Fungi*. Dover, 1962.

Lloyd, Francis Ernest, *The Carnivorous Plants*. Ronald, 1942.

Moldenke, Harold N. and Alma L., *Plants of the Bible*. Ronald, 1952.

Moore, Alma Chesnut, *The Grasses*. Macmillan, 1960.

Smith, Gilbert M., *Cryptogamic Botany* (2 vols., 2nd ed.). McGraw-Hill, 1955.

Thomas, William Sturgis, *Field Book of Common Mushrooms* (rev. ed.). G. P. Putnam's Sons, 1948.

Tiffany, L. H., *Algae, The Grass of Many Waters* (2nd ed.). Thomas, 1958.

Withner, Carl L., *The Orchids*. Ronald, 1959.

Environment and Distribution

Aubert de la Rüe, Edgar, François Bourlière and Jean-Paul Harroy, *The Tropics*. Alfred A. Knopf, 1957.

Dansereau, Pierre, *Biogeography*. Ronald, 1957.

Dasmann, Raymond F., *Environmental Conservation*. John Wiley & Sons, 1959.

Daubenmire, R. F., *Plants and Environment* (2nd ed.). John Wiley & Sons, 1959.

Haden-Guest, Stephen, John K. Wright and Eileen M. Teclaff, eds., *A World Geography of Forest Resources*. Ronald, 1956.

Mathews, F. Schuyler and Norman Taylor, *Field Book of American Wild Flowers* (rev. ed.). G. P. Putnam's Sons, 1955.

Oosting, Henry J., *The Study of Plant Communities*. W. H. Freeman, 1956.

Peattie, Donald Culross, *Flowering Earth*. Viking Press, 1961. *A Natural History of Western Trees*. Houghton Mifflin, 1953.

Richards, P. W., *The Tropical Rain Forest*. Cambridge University Press, 1952.

Vines, Robert H., *Trees, Shrubs and Woody Vines of the Southwest*. University of Texas Press, 1960.

Miscellaneous

Anderson, Edgar, *Plants, Man and Life*. Andrew Melrose, 1954.

*Bates, Marston, *The Forest and the Sea*. Random House, 1960.

Felt, Ephraim Porter, *Plant Galls and Gall Makers*. Comstock Publishing, 1940.

†Johnson, Willis H. and William C. Steere, eds., *This Is Life*. Holt, Rinehart & Winston, 1962.

Koeppe, Clarence E. and George C. De Long, *Weather and Climate*. McGraw-Hill, 1958.

Kramer, Paul J., *Plant and Soil Water Relationships*. McGraw-Hill, 1949.

May, Jacques M., *The Ecology of Malnutrition in the Far and Near East*, Hafner, 1961.

McCormick, Jack, *The Living Forest*. Harper & Row, 1959.

Meeuse, B.J.D., *The Story of Pollination*. Ronald, 1961.

Prentice, E. Parmalee, *Hunger and History*. Caxton, 1951.

†Scientific American, eds., *Plant Life*. Simon and Schuster, 1957.

Stevens, Neil E. and Russell B., *Disease in Plants*. Ronald, 1952.

Woytinsky, W. S. and E. S., *World Population and Production*. Twentieth Century Fund, 1953.

*Also available in paperback edition.

†Only available in paperback edition.

Credits

The sources for the illustrations in this book are shown below. Credits for pictures from left to right are separated by commas, top to bottom by dashes.

Cover—Alfred Eisenstaedt
8—Edmund B. Gerard
10—Eva Cellini
11—Tom Funk
12,13—Eric Gluckman
14,15—Eva Cellini
17—Elso S. Barghoorn, Dept. of Biology, Harvard University
18,19—Matt Greene
20,21—Alberto Querio, Dr. Pauline Shugaevsky and Eric Grave—Walter Dawn
22,23—Fritz Goro, Douglas F. Lawson, Dr. Ian K. Ross, William Costello—Dr. Ian K. Ross, Dr. Yata Haneda (2)
24—Charles R. Wyttenbach
25—Walter Dawn
26—Douglas Faulkner
27—Thomas M. Griffiths
28, 29—Irvin L. Oakes from Photo Researchers, Inc.
30 through 33—Anne Ophelia Todd Dowden
34—Douglas F. Lawson
36,37—Rudolf Freund
38,39—Matt Greene
43—Eric Grave from Photo Researchers, Inc.
44,45—Jack J. Kunz
46,47—Lee Boltin
48,49—Courtesy Carolina Biological Supply Co., Burlington, N.C.
50—The Davey Tree Expert Co., Kent, Ohio, Philip L. Feinberg; Fellow of the New York Microscopical Society—drawing by

Mark Binn—Robert Morton, Philip L. Feinberg
51—Philip L. Feinberg except center drawings by Mark Binn
52, 53—Lee Boltin, Philip L. Feinberg
54—Dr. A. E. Vatter; University of Colorado Medical Center
56, 57—Otto van Eersel
60—James Flora
61—Rudolf Freund
63—Jon Brenneis
64, 65—Mel Hunter
66—H. Lou Gibson—Bradley Smith
67—Lou Carrano—Bradley Smith
68—H. Lou Gibson—Bradley Smith
69—Russ Kinne from Photo Researchers, Inc.
70, 71—Jack Breed
72—Dr. Martin H. Zimmerman
75—Matt Greene
78, 79—Otto van Eersel
81—Dr. J. Arthur Herrick; Kent State University
82, 83—left: Lee Boltin; right: drawing by Otto van Eersel
84, 85—A. Y. Owen, Matt Greene
86—Lee Boltin—Horace Bristol
87—Dr. Vincent J. Schaefer
88, 89—Lee Boltin
90—W. D. Billings—David E. Scherman, Eliot Elisofon
91—Nevada State Highway Dept., Ansel Adams from Magnum—U.S. Forest Service,

Ansel Adams from Magnum
92, 93—Edmund B. Gerard
94—Mainichi Shimbun—Kay Tateishi
95—Jun Miki
96—John Dominis
99—Matt Greene
100—Matt Greene
101—René Martin
102—René Martin
103—Otto van Eersel
107—Jack Dermid
108, 109—J. T. Bonner,—D. Dennison Courtesy Smithsonian Institution, Edmund B. Gerard—Dr. R. M. Page
110, 111—Edmund B. Gerard
112—Lee Boltin—Edmund B. Gerard
113—Lee Boltin—Edmund B. Gerard
114, 115—Photos from *A Tree Is Born* by J. M. Guilcher and R. H. Noailles (Sterling) and Rapho-Guillumette
116, 117—R. H. Noailles and Rapho-Guillumette
118—C. Postma, Mozaiek van de Plant Courtesy H. J. W. Bechts' Uitgevers-Mij N.V.—Douglas F. Lawson
119—Douglas F. Lawson
120—Gabriel Moulin
125—René Martin
126, 127—Anthony D'Attilio
129—Mark Kauffman
130, 131—Mark Kauffman, Matt Greene

132 through 137—Mark Kauffman
138—Walter Dawn
142—Peg Estey
143—Anthony D'Attilio
144,145—Rudolf Freund
147—J. R. Eyerman
148,149—Shelly Grossman
150,151—Walter Dawn, Bradley Smith from Photo Researchers, Inc., Dr. L. A. Garay—Alfred Eisenstaedt
152—Irvin L. Oakes from Photo Researchers, Inc.
153—Dr. Ross E. Hutchins—C. Postma, Mozaiek van de Plant; Courtesy H.J.W. Bechts' Uitgevers-Mij N.V.
154—V. Argo—Dr. B. E. Juniper
155—Dr. David Pramer
156—Gordon S. Smith
157—Dr. Alexander B. Klots
158—Annan Photo Features
160—Walton C. Galinat
162—Jim Flora
169—Ralph Crane
170, 171—John Launois from Black Star
172,173—Eric Schaal
174,175—Dmitri Kessel
176,177—Rudolf Freund
178—Rudolf Freund
179—Al Fenn
180—J. R. Eyerman
181—Loomis Dean
183 through 187—John Langley Howard
Back Cover—Matt Greene

Acknowledgments

The editors of this book are particularly indebted to Richard M. Klein, Curator of Plant Physiology, New York Botanical Garden, who read the book in its entirety. They are also indebted to E. J. Alexander, Associate Curator, New York Botanical Garden; W. Dwight Billings, Professor of Botany, Duke University; Murray Buell, Professor of Botany, Rutgers University; Dale M. Coulson, Chairman, Analytical Research Department, Stanford Research Institute; Arthur Cronquist, Curator, New York Botanical Garden; Arthur C. Gentile, Associate Professor of Botany, University of Massachusetts; Sam Granick, Associate Professor of Biochemistry, Rockefeller Institute; John N. Hamlet; J. Arthur Herrick, Professor of Biological Sciences, Kent State University; S. H. Hutner, Haskins Laboratories; Lawrence Kaplan, Assistant Professor of Biology, Roosevelt University; M. W. Larson, Arizona-Sonora Desert Museum; Paul Mangelsdorf, Fisher Professor of Natural History, Harvard University; Jerome P. Miksche, Resident Fellow, Brookhaven Laboratory; Ross Nigrelli, Director of Research and Pathology, New York Aquarium; David J. Rogers, Curator of Quantitative Taxonomy, New York Botanical Garden; John B. Schmitt, Professor of Entomology, Rutgers University; William Campbell Steere, Director, New York Botanical Garden; Lewis Wayne Walker, Associate Director, Arizona-Sonora Desert Museum; U.S. Department of Agriculture.

Index

*Numerals in italics indicate a photograph
or painting of the subject mentioned.*

Index, *continued*

PRODUCTION STAFF FOR TIME INCORPORATED

Arthur R. Murphy Jr. (Vice President and Director of Production), Robert E. Foy, James P. Menton and Caroline Ferri

Text photocomposed under the direction of Albert J. Dunn and Arthur J. Dunn

✶

Printed by R. R. Donnelley & Sons Company, Crawfordsville, Indiana

Lithography by Livermore and Knight Co., a division of Printing Corporation of America, Providence, Rhode Island

Bound by R. R. Donnelley & Sons Company, Crawfordsville, Indiana

Paper by The Mead Corporation, Dayton, Ohio